Emma O'dowd

THE LANGUAGE GYM

SPANISH SENTENCE BUILDERS

A lexicogrammar approach

PRIMARY

THE LANGUAGE GYM

ISBN: 9783949651267

Imprint: Language Gym

Edited by:

Roberto Jover Soro & Inés Glowacka

About the authors

Simona Gravina has taught for 15 years, in schools in Italy and the UK, both in state and independent settings. She lives in Glasgow, Scotland. She is fluent in three languages and gets by in a few more. Simona is, besides a teacher, a mum, a bookworm, a passionate traveller and a fitness enthusiast. In the last couple of years she has been testing and implementing E.P.I. in one of the top Independent schools in Scotland, St Aloysius'College, where she is currently Modern Languages Curriculum Leader in the Junior School.

Stefano Pianigiani is currently teaching languages at Temple Moor High School in Leeds, England. He teaches Spanish, Italian and French being fluent in four languages and he is also learning others. In addition he is an educator at Nuestra Escuela Leeds, the first supplementary Spanish school in Yorkshire. Stefano is a fervent creator of resources whose greatest passions are cooking and DIY. He has a wide cultural experience having studied and lived in Italy, Spain and England. He has recently completed his MA in Education at Leeds Trinity University reinforcing his knowledge and competence on how to arouse engagement adopting the communicative approach within the classroom. He is an enthusiastic educator who has fully embraced Dr Conti's teaching from its origins. His academic interest has led him to becoming a governor at St. Nicholas Catholic Primary School.

Gianfranco Conti taught for 25 years at schools in Italy, the UK and in Kuala Lumpur, Malaysia. He has also been a university lecturer, holds a Master's degree in Applied Linguistics and a PhD in metacognitive strategies as applied to second language writing. He is now an author, a popular independent educational consultant and a professional development provider. He has written around 2,000 resources for the TES website, which have awarded him the Best Resources Contributor in 2015. He has co-authored the best-selling and influential book for world languages teachers, "The Language Teacher Toolkit", "Breaking the sound barrier: Teaching learners how to listen", in which he puts forth his Listening As Modelling methodology and "Memory: what every language teacher should know". Last but not least, Gianfranco has created the instructional approach known as E.P.I. (Extensive Processing Instruction).

Dylan Viñales has taught for 15 years, in schools in Bath, Beijing and Kuala Lumpur in state, independent and international settings. He lives in Kuala Lumpur. He is fluent in five languages, and gets by in several more. Dylan is, besides a teacher, a professional development provider, specialising in E.P.I., metacognition, teaching languages through music (especially ukulele) and cognitive science. In the last five years, together with Dr Conti, he has driven the implementation of E.P.I. in one of the top international schools in the world: Garden International School. Dylan authors an influential blog on modern language pedagogy in which he supports the teaching of languages through E.P.I.

DEDICATION

For my daughter Giulia
-Simona

For my family & Deirdre Jones
-Stefano

For Catrina
-Gianfranco

For Ariella & Leonard
-Dylan

Acknowledgements

Creating a book is a time-consuming yet rewarding endeavour.

Simona would like to thank her daughter Giulia, currently a Primary student, for all her encouragement and for actively testing and giving feedback on the tasks. Huge gratitude to her twin Primary teacher Emanuela for feedback on specific tasks.
Secondly, she would like to thank at St Aloysius' College, especially Giulia Frisina for all the contributions and advice in testing the tasks as a trained E.P.I. teacher, who has fully implemented Dr. Conti's methodology in the classroom.

Stefano is indebted to his English mother Maria who has offered her constant help in the choice of words and correct use of the language. He would also like to thank his eagle-eyed pupils at Temple Moor High School for their full engagement and enthusiasm in experimenting with the tasks.

We would like to thank our editors, Roberto Jover Soro and Inés Glowacka, for their tireless work, proofreading, editing and advising on this book. They are talented, accomplished professionals who work at the highest possible level and add value at every stage of the process. Not only this, but they are also lovely, good-humoured colleagues who go above and beyond, and make the hours of collaborating a real pleasure. Gracias a los dos.

Our sincere gratitude to all the people involved in the recording of the Listening audio files:
Ariella, Lenny and Natasha Viñales, Carlota Viguer Seriñá, Dacho Ball & Roberto Jover Soro. Your energy, enthusiasm and passion comes across clearly in every recording and is the reason why the listening sections are such a successful and engaging resource, according to the many students who have been alpha and beta testing the book. In addition, our gratitude to Chris Koelma for his moral support and for sharing his expertise of sound recording and digital mastering. You added heaps of value and, more importantly, helped keep Dylan relatively sane at crucial moments during the sound editing process!

Thanks to Flaticon.com and Mockofun.com for providing access to a limitless library of engaging icons, clipart and images which we have used to make this book more user-friendly than any other Sentence Builders predecessor, with a view to be as engaging as possible for primary level students.

Finally, our gratitude to the MFL Twitterati for their ongoing support of E.P.I. and the Sentence Builders book series. In particular a shoutout to our team of incredible educators who helped in checking all the units: Aurélie Lethuilier, Nadim Cham, Joe Barnes-Moran, Dannielle Warren, Carmen Aguilar, Tom Ball, Jérôme Nogue, Valle Fernandez, Esmeralda Salgado, Verónica Palacin, Ester Borin and Jaume Llorens. It is thanks to your time, patience, professionalism and detailed feedback that we have been able to produce such a refined and highly accurate product.

Gracias a todos,
Simona, Stefano, Gianfranco & Dylan

Introduction

Hello and welcome to the first Sentence Builders workbook designed for Primary aged children, designed to be an accompaniment to a Spanish Extensive Processing Instruction course. The book has come about out of necessity, because such a resource did not previously exist.

How to use this book if you have bought into our E.P.I. approach

This book was originally designed as a resource to use in conjunction with our E.P.I. approach and teaching strategies. Our course favours flooding comprehensible input, organising content by communicative functions and related constructions, and a big focus on reading and listening as modelling. The aim of this book is to empower the beginner learner with linguistic tools - high-frequency structures and vocabulary - useful for real-life communication. Since, in a typical E.P.I. unit of work, aural and oral work play a huge role, this book should not be viewed as the ultimate E.P.I. coursebook, but rather as a **useful resource** to **complement** your Listening-As-Modelling and Speaking activities.

Sentence Builders – Online Versions

Please note that all these sentence builders will be available in bilingual and Spanish only versions on the Language Gym website, available to download, editable and in landscape design optimised for displaying in the classroom, via the ***Locker Room** section.

**Please note that the Locker Room is only accessible via a paid subscription or as part of a full Language Gym Licence.*

How to use this book if you don't know or have NOT bought into our approach

Alternatively, you may use this book to dip in and out of as a source of printable material for your lessons. Whilst our curriculum is driven by communicative functions rather than topics, we have deliberately embedded the target constructions in topics which are popular with teachers and commonly found in published coursebooks.

If you would like to learn about E.P.I. you could read one of the authors' blogs. The definitive guide is Dr Conti's "Patterns First – How I Teach Lexicogrammar" which can be found on his blog (www.gianfrancoconti.com). There are also blogs on Dylan's wordpress site (mrvinalesmfl.wordpress.com) such as "Using sentence builders to reduce (everyone's) workload and create more fluent linguists" which can be read to get teaching ideas and to learn how to structure a course, through all the stages of E.P.I.

Examples of E.P.I. activities and games to play in class, based on MARS EARS sequence, can be found in Simona's padlet (https://en-gb.padlet.com/simograv/svi55fluxeolisi9) "MFL Teaching based on E.P.I. approach, Videos and blogs, Sample activities from Modelling to Spontaneity". These can be used to model tasks.

The book "Breaking the Sound Barrier: Teaching Learners how to Listen" by Gianfranco Conti and Steve Smith, provides a detailed description of the approach and of the listening and speaking activities you can use in synergy with the present book.

The structure of the book

This book contains 10 units which concern themselves with a specific communicative function, such as 'I can say my name and age', 'I can talk about the weather', 'I can say what's in my town'. You can find a note of each communicative function in the Table of Contents. Each unit includes:

- a sentence builder modelling the target constructions, introduced by questions to guide communication;
- a set of Listening-As-Modelling activities to train decoding skills, sound awareness, speech-segmentation, lexical-retrieval and parsing skills;
- a set of reading tasks focusing on both the meaning and structural levels of the text;
- a set of translation tasks aimed at consolidation through retrieval practice;
- a set of writing tasks targeting essential writing micro-skills such as spelling, functional and positional processing, editing and communication of meaning.

Each sentence builder at the beginning of a unit contains one or more constructions which have been selected with real-life communication in mind. Each unit is built around that construction but not solely on it. Based on the principle that each E.P.I instructional sequence must move from modelling to production in a seamless and organic way, each unit expands on the material in each sentence builder by embedding it in texts and graded tasks which contain both familiar and unfamiliar (but comprehensible and learnable) vocabulary and structures. Through lots of careful recycling and thorough and extensive processing of the input, by the end of each unit the student has many opportunities to encounter and process the new vocabulary and patterns with material from the previous units.

Alongside the units you will find: No Snakes No Ladders tasks created to practise speaking skills with an engaging and fun board game that can be photocopied and played in groups of 3 students.

Important *caveat*

1) This is a '**no frills**' book. This means that there are a limited number of illustrations. This is because we want every single little thing in this book to be useful. We have given serious thought to both **recycling** and **interleaving**, in order to allow for key constructions, words and grammar items to be revisited regularly so as to enhance exponentially their retention.

2) **Listening** as modelling is an essential part of E.P.I. The listening files for each listening unit can be found in the AUDIO section on Language-Gym.com - a subscription to the website is **not required** to access these.

3) **All content** in this booklet matches the content on the **Language Gym** website. For best results, we recommend a mixture of communicative, retrieval practice games, combined with Language Gym games and workouts, and then this booklet as the follow-up, either in class or for homework.

4) This booklet is suitable for **beginner** learners. This equates to a **CEFR A1-A2** level, or a beginner **KS2 (or a less strong KS3)** class. You do not need to start at the beginning, although you may want to dip in to certain units for revision/recycling. You do not need to follow the booklet in order, although many of you will, and if you do, you will benefit from the specific recycling/interleaving strategies. Either way, all topics are repeated frequently throughout the book.

We do hope that you and your students will find this book useful and enjoyable.

Table of Contents

UNIT 1

ME LLAMO

In this unit you will learn how to say in Spanish:

- ✓ What your name is
- ✓ How old you are
- ✓ Hello and good morning
- ✓ Numbers 1 to 12

Hola, ¿cómo te llamas?

Me llamo Inés

UNIT 1. ME LLAMO

I can say my name and age

¿Cómo te llamas? *What's your name?*
¿Cuántos años tienes? *How old are you?*

Hola *Hello*	me llamo *my name is*	Ana	y *and*	tengo *I have**	un *1*	año *year*
		Belén				
		Carlos				
		David			dos 2	años years
		Esmeralda			tres 3	
Buenos días *Good morning*		Felipe			cuatro 4	
		Guillermo			cinco 5	
		Inés			seis 6	
		José			siete 7	
		Juan			ocho 8	
		Jimena			nueve 9	
		María			diez 10	
		Nieves			once 11	
		Patricia			doce 12	
		Pedro				
		Roberto				
		Sofía				
		Valle				

***Author's note.** In Spanish you do not say *I am five years old* but *I have 5 years.*
e.g. Tengo cinco años

Unit 1. My name and age: LISTENING

1. Listen and complete with the missing vowel

a. Me llam__

b. T__ngo

c. Se__s

d. Cinc__

e. C__atro

f. Añ__s

g. __no

h. Onc__

i. D__ez

j. Si__te

a	*e*	*i*	*o*	*u*

2. Can you help the penguin to break the flow?

Draw a line between words

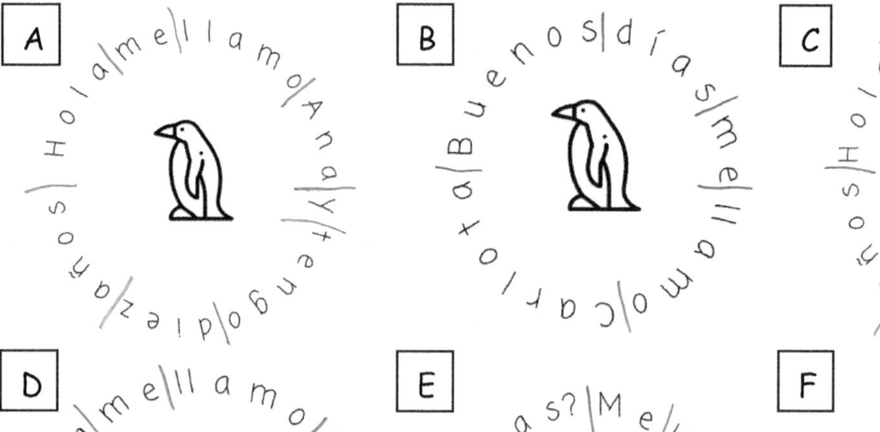

A: Holamellamo Anaytengodiezaños

B: Buenosdíasmellamo Carlota

C: Holamellamo Felipe Tengoochoaños

D: Holamellamo Joséytengodoceaños

E: ¿Cómotellamas? Mellamo Jimena

F: ¿Cuántosañostienes? Tengoseisaños

3. Listen and tick one option for each sentence ✓

		1	2	3
a.	Me llamo	Pedro	Pablo	Pilar
b.	Tengo	once años	dos años	cuatro años
c.	Tengo	diez años	doce años	ocho años
d.	Hola	buenos días	¿Cuántos años tienes?	¿Cómo te llamas?

4. Complete with the missing syllables in the box below

a. ¿Cómo te lla ___ ?

b. Me ___ mo Esmeralda.

c. Ten ___ cinco años.

d. Bue ___ días.

e. Ho ___ , me llamo José.

f. ¿Cuántos años ___ nes?

g. ___ go siete años.

h. Tengo do ___ años.

i. Me lla ___ Gui ___ rmo.

j. Hola, me llamo S ___ ía.

of	tie	go	mo	la	mas	lla	nos	ce	ten	lle

5. Fill in the grid with the correct information

	Name	Age (Number)
a.		
b.		
c.		
d.		

6. Faulty Echo

e.g. Tengo <u>seis</u> años.

a. Tengo nueve años.

b. Hola, tengo doce años.

c. Buenos días, me llamo María.

d. Hola, tengo once años.

e. Hola, me llamo Guillermo y tengo ocho años.

f. Me llamo Juan y tengo siete años.

g. ¿Cuántos años tienes?

7. Track the sounds

Listen and write down how many times you will hear the sound

1.	a	
2.	e	
3.	i	
4.	o	
5.	u	

8. Spot the Intruder

Identify and underline the word in each sentence the speaker is NOT saying

e.g. Me llamo Ana <u>hola</u>.

a. ¿Cómo te llamas? No me llamo Pedro.

b. ¿Cuántos años tienes? Tengo tres seis años.

c. Buenas tardes, tengo me llamo Beatriz.

d. Hola José, y ¿Cuántos años tienes?

e. Hola, dos me llamo Ana y tengo diez años.

9. Spelling Challenge (1-12)

Listen and complete the Spanish words with the missing letter.

a.	D__s	g.	Oc__o
b.	U__o	h.	T__es
c.	S__is	i.	Cua__ro
d.	Nu__ve	j.	Si__te
e.	C__nco	k.	Do__e
f.	Die__	l.	O__ce

10. Listen and circle the correct number (1-12)

e.g. ¿Cuántos años tienes? Tengo nueve años

e.g.	*7*	*8*	*9*
a.	6	7	8
b.	10	3	2
c.	9	12	11
d.	4	5	1
e.	12	6	4

Unit 1. My name and age: VOCABULARY BUILDING

1. Match Up

1. Me llamo
2. Diez
3. Tres
4. Cuatro
5. Dos
6. Trece
7. Once
8. Años
9. Cinco
10. Siete

a. Ten
b. Four
c. Two
d. Five
e. My name is
f. Seven
g. Three
h. Thirteen
i. Years
j. Eleven

1	
2	
3	
4	
5	
6	
7	
8	
9	
10	

2. Broken Words

a. Ten____ *I have*
b. O____ *Eight*
c. Se____ *Six*
d. A____ *Years*
e. Me lla____ *My name is*
f. Do____ *Twelve*
g. U____ *One*
h. Sie____ *Seven*
i. Nue____ *Nine*
j. Di____ *Ten*

3. Complete the sentences with the missing words below

a. Tengo ____________ años. *I am seven years old.*
b. Me ____________ Dylan. *My name is Dylan.*
c. Tengo ____________ años. *I am eleven years old.*
d. ¿Cómo ______ llamas? *What is your name?*
e. ¿Cuántos años ____________? *What age are you?*
f. ____________, me llamo Nieves. *Hello, my name is Nieves.*
g. ¿Cómo se escribe tu ____________? *How do you write your name?*
h. Me llamo Ana y ____________ trece años. *My name is Ana and I am 13.*

tienes	llamo	nombre	siete	te	hola	once	tengo

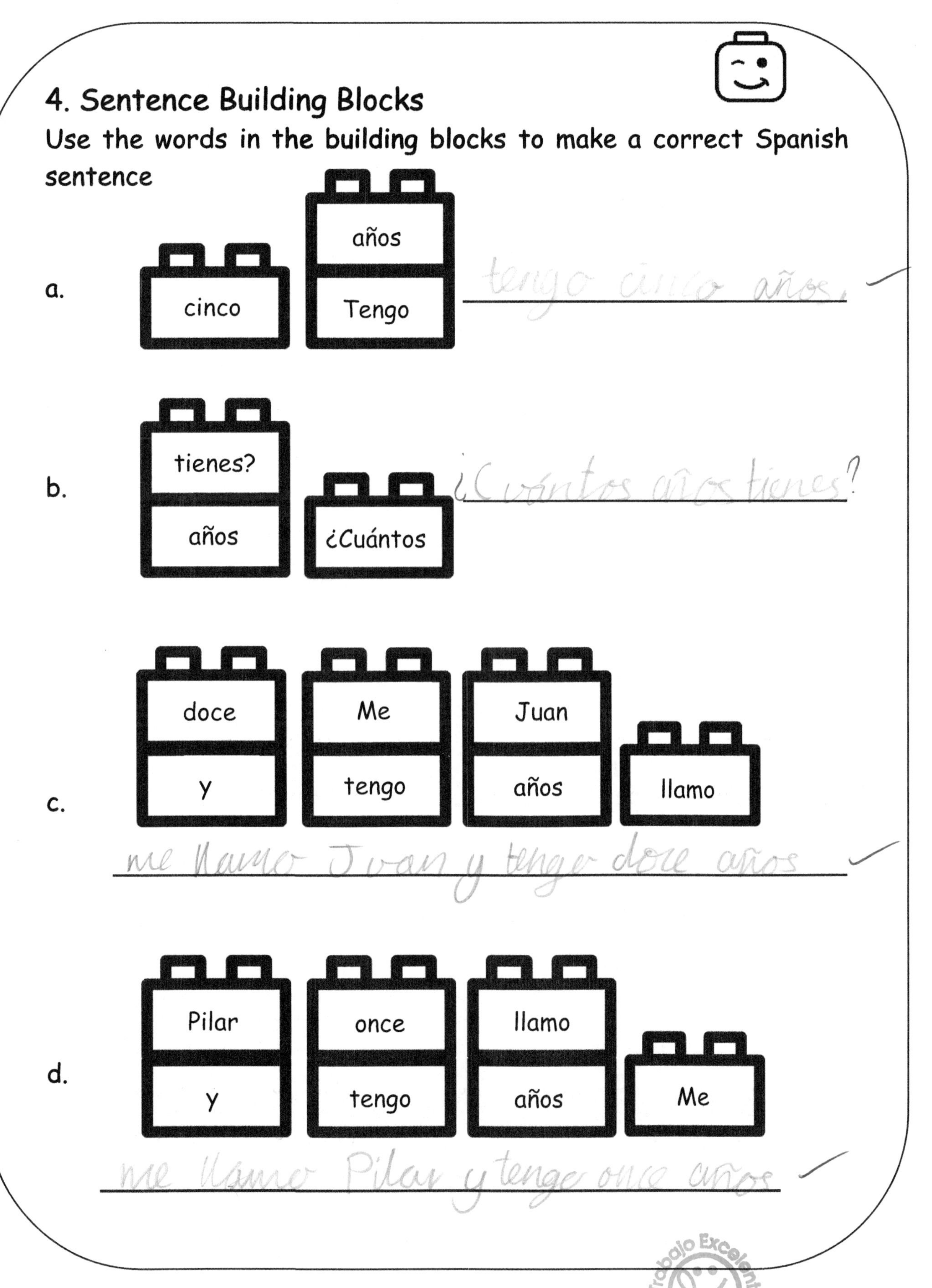

4. Sentence Building Blocks

Use the words in the building blocks to make a correct Spanish sentence

a. cinco | años / Tengo

tengo cinco años.

b. tienes? / años | ¿Cuántos

¿Cuántos años tienes?

c. doce / y | Me / tengo | Juan / años | llamo

me llamo Juan y tengo doce años

d. Pilar / y | once / tengo | llamo / años | Me

me llamo Pilar y tengo once años

¡Trabajo Excelente!

Unit 1. My name and age: READING

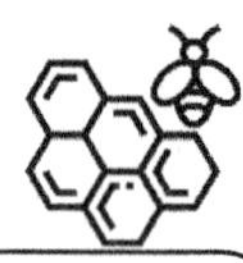

1. Sylla-Bees
   Translate the phrases putting the cells in the correct order

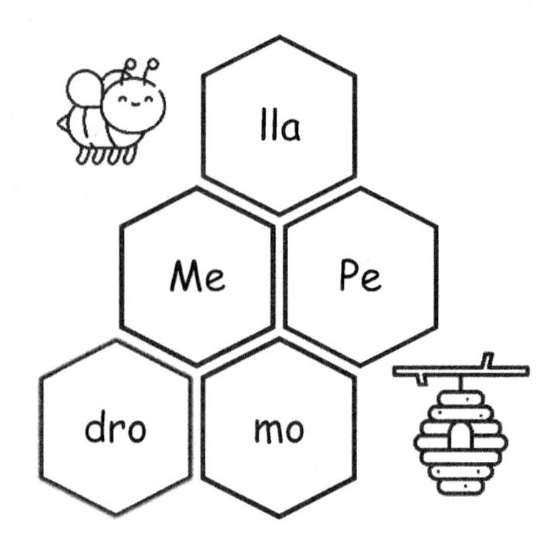

a. *My name is Pedro.*

M __ ll__ __ __ P__ __ __ __

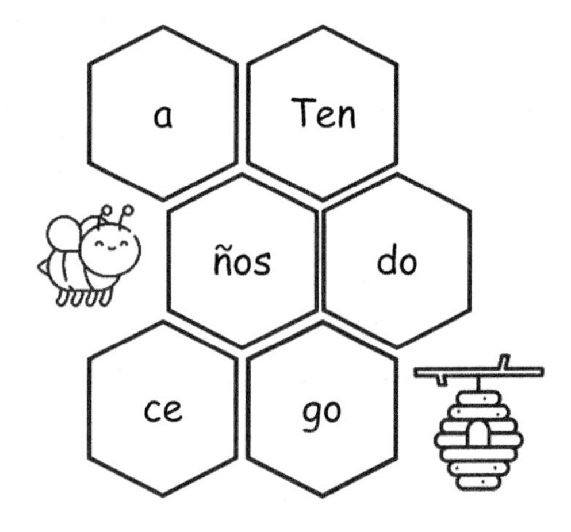

b. *I am 12 years old.*

T__ __ __ __ d__ __ __

a__ __ __

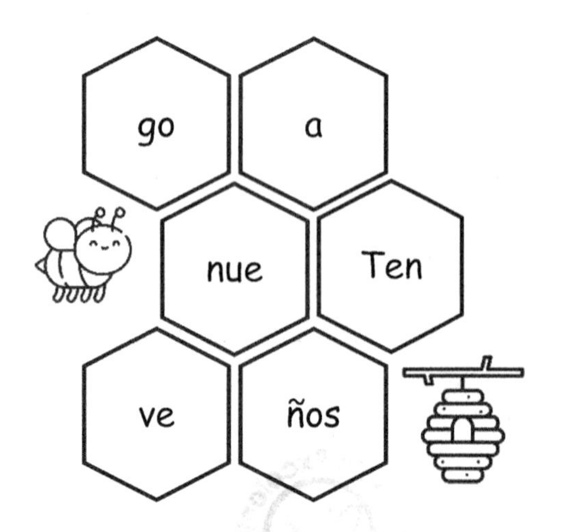

c. *I am 9 years old.*

__ __ __ __ __ __ __ __ __ __

__ __ __ __

2. True or False ✓

Read the dialogues below and for each statement tick

1a. Hola, ¿Cómo te llamas? Yo me llamo Enrique.

1b. Hola, me llamo Carlota. ¿Cuántos años tienes?

1c. Tengo diez años, ¿y tú?

1d. Tengo ocho años.

2a. Buenos días, ¿Cómo te llamas? Yo me llamo Estéfano.

2b. Hola, me llamo Amira. ¿Cuántos años tienes?

2c. Tengo doce años, ¿y tú?

2d. Tengo once años.

	True	False
1a. His name is **Enrique**.	✓	
1b. Her name is **Carla**.		✓
1c. He is 11 years old.		✓
1d. She is 8 years old.	✓	
2a. His name is **Pablo**.		✓
2b. Her name is **Amira**.	✓	
2c. He is 12 years old.	✓	
2d. She is 10 years old.		✓

8/8

Unit 1. My name and age: WRITING

1. Spelling

a. M ___ ll ___ ___ ___ — *My name is...*

b. T ___ n ___ ___ d ___ ez añ ___ ___ — *I am ten years old.*

c. C ___ ___ tro ___ ños — *Four years.*

d. N ___ ___ ___ e a ___ ___ ___ — *Nine years.*

e. ¿Có ___ ___ t ___ ll ___ ___ ___ s? — *What's your name?*

f. ¿Cuá ___ ___ ___ s años t ___ ___ nes? — *How old are you?*

g. ¿ ___ óm ___ se e ___ ___ ___ ibe tu nombre? — *How do you spell your name?*

2. Anagrams

a. ogneT coho ñoas — *I am 8 years old.*

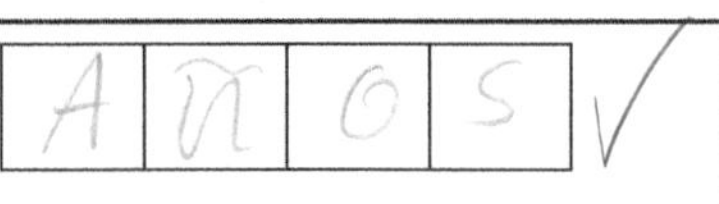

b. eM allom aMíar — *My name is Maria.*

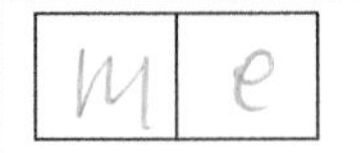

c. Togne oedc sñoa — *I am twelve years old.*

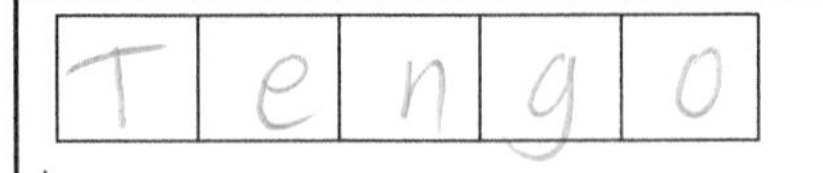

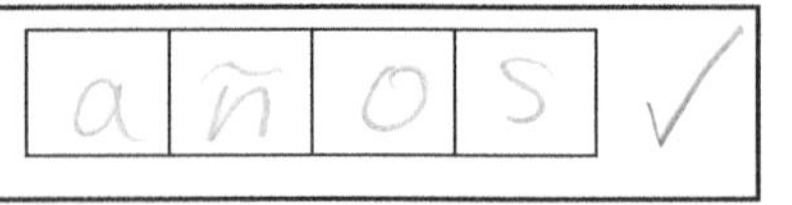

d. engTo setie osña — *I am seven years old.*

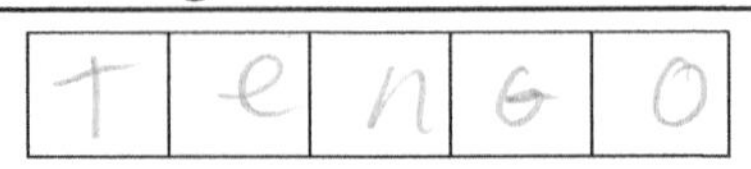

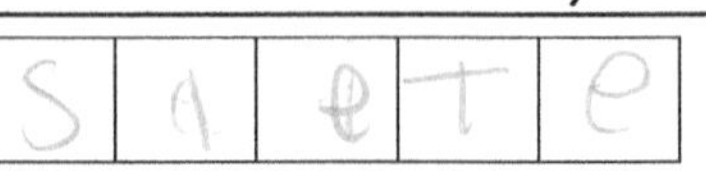

e. gonTe ceno asño — *I am eleven years old.*

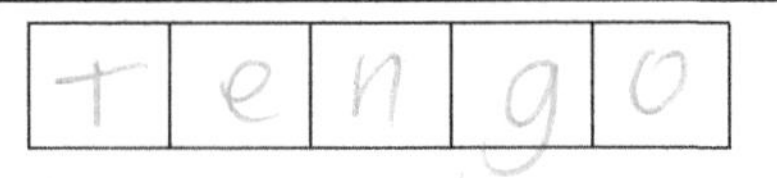

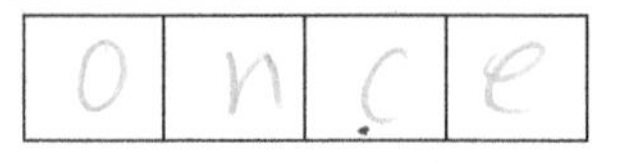

hola hi

3. Faulty Translation. Write the correct English version.

e.g. Tengo diez años.	*I am 11 years old.*	*I am 10 years old*
a. Tengo siete años.	I am 6 years old.	
b. ¿Cómo se escribe?	What's your name?	
c. ¿Cuántos años tienes?	How do you spell it?	
d. ¿Cómo te llamas?	How old are you?	
e. Hola, me llamo Ana.	Bye, my name's Ana.	

4. Phrase-level Translation. How would you say it in Spanish?

a. I am 8 years old. ____________________

b. My name is... ____________________

c. What's your name? ____________________

d. I am 12 years old. ____________________

e. How old are you? ____________________

f. Good morning. ____________________

g. Hello. ____________________

h. How do you spell it? ____________________

UNIT 1 - ME LLAMO (My name and age)

LISTENING

1. Listen and complete with the missing vowel

a. Me llamo b. Tengo c. Seis d. Cinco e. Cuatro f. Años g. Uno h. Once i. Diez j. Siete

2. Can you help the penguin to break the flow?

a. Hola, me llamo Ana y tengo diez años.
b. Buenos días, me llamo Carlota.
c. Hola, me llamo Felipe. Tengo ocho años.
d. Hola, me llamo José y tengo doce años.
e. ¿Cómo te llamas? Me llamo Jimena.
f. ¿Cuántos años tienes? Tengo siete años.

3. Listen and tick one option for each sentence

a. 2 Me llamo Pablo. b. 1 Tengo once años. c. 3 Tengo ocho años. d. 3 Hola, ¿Cómo te llamas?

4. Complete with the missing syllables in the box below

a. ¿Cómo te llamas?
b. Me llamo Esmeralda.
c. Tengo cinco años.
d. Buenos días.
e. Hola, me llamo José.
f. ¿Cuántos años tienes?
g. Tengo siete años.
h. Tengo doce años.
i. Me llamo Guillermo.
j. Hola, me llamo Sofía.

5. Fill in the grid with the correct name and age

a. Me llamo Valle. Tengo ocho años. **Valle ; 8**
b. Buenos días, me llamo José. Tengo seis años. **José ; 6**
c. Hola, Me llamo Sofía y tengo once años. **Sofía ; 11**
d. ¿Cómo te llamas? Me llamo Pedro y tengo siete años. **Pedro ; 7**

6. Faulty Echo.

a. Tengo nueve años. (anos)
b. Hola, tengo doce años. (doche)
c. Buenos días, me llamo María. (Buenas)
d. Hola, tengo once años. (onche)
e. Hola, me llamo Guillermo y tengo ocho años. (lamo)
f. Me llamo Juan y tengo siete años. (Gyuan)
g. ¿Cuántos años tienes? (tenes)

7. Track the sounds: Listen and write down how many times you will hear the sound

1. **A: 7 times** Hola, Me Llamo, García, Cinco, Años, Ana
2. **E: 8 times** Siete, Nueve, Pedro, Cómo, Buenos, Tienes, Uno
3. **I: 6 times** Pilar, Seis, Tres, María, Ignacio, Ocho, Buenos Días,
4. **O: 7 times** Once, José, Dos, Te Llamas, Tengo, Carlos, Ocho, Nina
5. **U: 7 times** Cuatro, Nueve, Uno, Carmen, Raúl, Cuántos, Cumpleaños, Juan

8. Spot the Intruder.

Identify and underline the word in each sentence the speaker is NOT saying

e.g. Me llamo Ana hola. ***hola***
a. ¿Cómo te llamas? No me llamo Pedro. **no**
b. ¿Cuántos años tienes? Tengo tres seis años. **tres**
c. Buenas tardes, tengo me llamo Beatriz. **tengo**
d. Hola José, y ¿Cuántos años tienes? **y**
e. Hola, dos me llamo Ana y tengo diez años. **dos**

9. Spelling Challenge (1-12) Listen and complete the Spanish words with the missing letter.

a. Dos b. Uno c. Seis d. Nueve e. Cinco f. Diez
g. Ocho h. Tres i. Cuatro j. Siete k. Doce l. Once

10. Listen and circle the correct number

a. Siete, 7 b. Diez, 10 c. Once, 11 d. Cinco, 5 e. Doce, 12

VOCABULARY BUILDING

1 . Match Up

1. e 2. a 3. g 4. b 5. c 6. h 7. j 8. i 9. d 10. f

2. Broken Words

a. Tengo b. Ocho c. Seis d. Años e. Me llamo f. Doce g. Uno h. Siete i. Nueve j. Diez

3. Complete the sentences with the missing words below

a. Tengo **siete** años. b. Me **llamo** Dylan. c. Tengo **once** años.
d. ¿Cómo **te** llamas? e. ¿Cuántos años **tienes**? f. **Hola**, me llamo Nieves.
g. ¿Cómo se escribe tu **nombre**? h. Me llamo Ana y **tengo** trece años.

4. Sentence Building Blocks

a. Tengo cinco años. b. ¿Cuántos años tienes?
c. Me llamo Juan y tengo doce años. d. Me llamo Pilar y tengo once años.

READING

1. Sylla-Bees

a . Me llamo Pedro. b. Tengo doce años. c. Tengo nueve años.

2. True or False

1a. True 1b. False (Carlota) 1c. False (10) 1d. True
2a. False (Estéfano) 2b. True 2c. True 2d. False (11)

WRITING

1. Spelling

a. Me llamo... b. Tengo diez años. c. Cuatro años d. Nueve años e. ¿Cómo te llamas?
f. ¿Cuántos años tienes? g. ¿Cómo se escribe tu nombre?

2. Anagrams

a. Tengo ocho años. b. Me llamo María. c. Tengo doce años. d. Tengo siete años. e. Tengo once años.

3. Faulty Translation

a. I am **7** years old. b. **How do you spell** your name? c. How **old are you**?
d. **What's your name**? e. **Hello,** my name's Ana.

4. Phrase-level Translation

a. Tengo ocho años. b. Me llamo. c. ¿Cómo te llamas? d. Tengo doce años. e. ¿Cuántos años tienes?
f. Buenos días. g. Hola. h. ¿Cómo se escribe?

UNIT 2

EL ALFABETO

In this unit you will learn to:

- ✓ Spell your name in Spanish
- ✓ Practise Spanish sounds

You will revisit:

- ★ Saying your name and age
- ★ How to count from 1 to 12

¿Cómo se escribe tu nombre?

Se escribe S-A-R-A

UNIT 2. ALPHABET AND PHONICS.
I can hear and pronounce Spanish sounds

¿Cómo se escribe tu nombre? *How do you spell your name?*

1. Listen and write the alphabet as you hear it.

Mi nombre se escribe *My name is spelt*				
	A	*<ah>*	Ñ	nee
	B	beh	O	oh
	C	theh	P	peh
	D	deh	Q	kooh
	E	eh	R	ereh
	F	efeh	S	eseh
	G	heh (serrated h)	T	teh
	H	achheh	U	oo
	I	ee	V	oobeh
	J	hotah	W	oobeh doblah
	K	kah	X	ekees
	L	eleh	Y	eegriegah
	M	emeh	Z	thetah
	N	eneh		

2. Fill in the gaps: ¿Cómo se ecribe? *How is it spelt?*

a. C __ r l o s

b. F e l __ p e

c. __ u a n

d. A l e __ a n d r o

e. C r __ s t i n a

f. L e t i __ i a

g. S o __ í a

h. P __ d r o

i. J o __ é

j. V a __ __ e

3. Complete the words with the missing letters

a. ¿Cóm__ s__ escrib __ t__ n__mbre?

b. Me ll__mo __aría.

c. M__ llamo B__lén.

d. M__ nombr__ se es__ribe.

e. Me __amo __osé.

4. Listen and choose the correct spelling

	1	2
a.	Me lyamo	Me llamo
b.	Años	Anos
c.	Huan	Juan
d.	Cumpleanios	Cumpleaños
e.	Español	Espanyol
f.	Hoolia	Julia
g.	José	Kosé
h.	Amarilo	Amarillo
i.	Ninos	Niños
j.	Guillermo	Guilermo

5. Listen and tick the letter you hear

1.	C	G	Z
2.	F	S	H
3.	L	H	J
4.	Ñ	N	M
5.	I	E	A
6.	K	C	S
7.	X	H	V
8.	U	V	W

6. Listen and write the names being spelled out:

1. _ _ _ _ _ _
2. _ _ _ _ _ _
3. _ _ _ _
4. _ _ _ _ _
5. _ _ _ _ _
6. _ _ _ _ _ _ _
7. _ _ _ _ _ _
8. _ _ _ _ _ _

No Snakes No Ladders

Unit 1-2

SALIDA	1 Hola	2 Me llamo	3 Me llamo Carlos	4 ¿Cómo te llamas?	5 Buenos días	6 Me llamo Pedro	7 y
15 Me llamo Patricia	14 Tengo ocho años	13 ¿Cuántos años tienes ?	12 Tengo nueve años	11 Tengo once años	10 Me llamo María	9 Me llamo Felipe	8 Tengo siete años
16 Tengo diez años	17 Me llamo Guillermo	18 ¿Cómo se escribe?	19 Buenas tardes	20 Tengo cinco años	21 Me llamo Sofía	22 Tengo seis años	23 Hola, me llamo...
LLEGADA	30 Buenos días Ana	29 Hola Juan	28 Tengo cuatro años	27 Me llamo Carlota	26 Me llamo Nieves	25 Tengo doce años	24 Me llamo José

No Snakes No Ladders

SALIDA	1 Hello	2 My name is	3 My name is Carlos	4 What's your name?	5 Good morning	6 My name is Pedro	7 and
15 My name is Patricia	14 I am 8 years old	13 How old are you?	12 I am 9 years old	11 I am 11 years old	10 My name is María	9 My name is Felipe	8 I am 7 years old
16 I am 10 years old	17 My name is Guillermo	18 How do you spell it?	19 Good afternoon	20 I am 5 years old	21 My name is Sofía	22 I am 6 years old	23 Hello, my name is...
LLEGADA	30 Good morning Ana	29 Hello Juan	28 I am 4 years old	27 My name is Carlota	26 My name is Nieves	25 I am 12 years old	24 My name is José

UNIT 2 - ALPHABET AND PHONICS

LISTENING

1. Listen and write the alphabet as you hear it.

(Mi nombre se escribe...)

No fixed answer. Students write down letters of the alphabet and compare them with their classmates. Whole-class discussion.

2. Fill in the gaps with the missing letters

Transcript: "Se escribe..."

a. Carlos b. Felipe c. Juan d. Alejandro e. Cristina f. Leticia g. Sofía h. Pedro i. José j. Valle

3. Complete the words with the missing letters

a. ¿Cómo se escribe tu nombre? b. Me llamo María. c. Me llamo Belén. d. Mi nombre se escribe... e. Me llamo José.

4. Listen and choose the correct spelling

a. 1 - Me llamo b. 2 - Años c. 2 - Juan d. 2 - Cumpleaños e. 1 - Español f. 2 - Julia g. 1 - José h. 2 - Amarillo i. 2 - Niños j. 1 - Guillermo

5. Listen and tick the letter you hear

1. G 2. H 3. J 4. Ñ 5. E 6. C 7. V 8. U

6. Listen and write the names being spelled out:

1. Carlos
2. Carmen
3. Juan
4. María
5. Pedro
6. Antonio
7. Nieves
8. Jimena

UNIT 3

¿CÓMO ESTÁS?

In this unit you will learn how to say in Spanish:

✓ How you are

You will revisit:

★ What is your name
★ Saying your age
★ 'Hello' and 'Good morning'

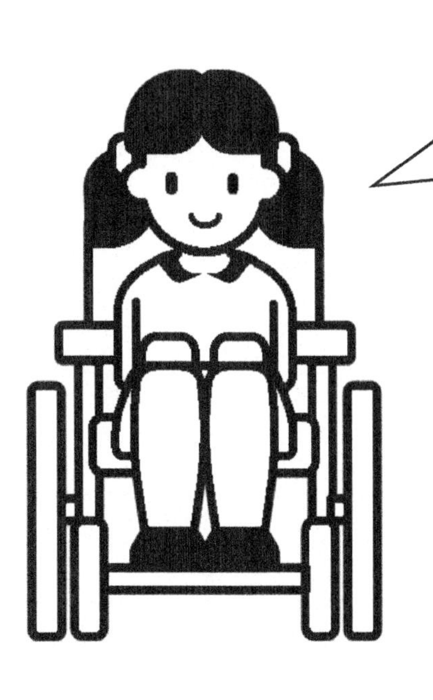

Hola, ¿qué tal?

Estoy muy bien, gracias.

UNIT 3. ¿CÓMO ESTÁS?

I can greet and say how I am

¿Qué tal?/¿Cómo estás? *How are you?*

				MASC	FEM
Hola *Hello* Buenos días *Good morning* Buenas tardes *Good afternoon* Buenas noches *Good evening / Good night*	estoy *I am*	fenomenal *great* muy bien *very well* bien *well* regular *so-so* mal *bad* fatal *awful*	porque estoy *because I am*	cansado *tired* contento *cheerful* estresado *stressed* feliz *happy* nervioso *nervous* relajado *relaxed* tranquilo *calm* triste *sad*	cansada *tired* contenta *cheerful* estresada *stressed* feliz *happy* nerviosa *nervous* relajada *relaxed* tranquila *calm* triste *sad*
Gracias *Thank you*					

*Author's note: "**Estoy**" means "**I am**". It is often used to talk about how you are feeling or how you are.*

Unit 3. I can greet and say how I am: LISTENING

1. Listen and tick the word you hear

	1	2	3
e.g.	*Buenos días* ✓	*Hola*	*Buenas tardes*
a.	Regular	Mal	Bien
b.	Tranquilo	Triste	Tranquila
c.	Contento	Cansado	Contenta
d.	Cansado	Fatal	Cansada
e.	Estresado	Estresada	Feliz

2. Listen and complete with the missing vowel

a. Estoy content___.

b. Buen___s noches.

c. Estoy tranquil___.

d. Buen___s tardes.

e. Estoy f___nomenal.

f. ___stoy triste.

g. Estoy cansad___.

h. Hola, m___ llamo Roberto.

i. Estoy muy b___en.

j. B___enos días.

k. Estoy f___tal.

l. Estoy relajad___.

m. Estoy nervios___.

n. Buenos d___as.

3. Complete with the missing syllables in the box below

a. Estoy es _ _ _ sado.

b. Estoy _ _ en.

c. Bue _ _ _ días.

d. Bue _ _ _ tardes.

e. Estoy muy bi _ _.

f. Estoy bien por _ _ _ estoy feliz.

g. Estoy conten _ _.

h. Hola, me _ _ _ mo María.

i. Es _ _ _ cansada.

j. Estoy mal porque estoy ner _ _ _ so.

tre	nas	nos	que	bi	toy	en	lla	to	vio

4. Listen and choose the correct spelling

	a	b
1.	Buenos días	Buenas días
2.	Estoe	Estoy
3.	Buenos tardes	Buenas tardes
4.	Nervioso	Nerviouso
5.	Bein	Bien
6.	Feleez	Feliz
7.	Tranquilo	Trankeelo
8.	Porkwe	Porque
9.	Qui tal	Qué tal
10.	Relajada	Relahada

5. Break the flow: Draw a line between words

a. Estoymuybienporqueestoyfeliz

b. Estoymalporqueestoycansado

c. Holaestoymalporqueestoytriste

d. ¿Quétal?Estoyregulargracias

e. HolamellamoJoséyestoybien

6. Fill in the grid with the correct information in English

	Greeting	Emotion
e.g. Pablo	*Hello*	*Happy*
a. Nieves	good morning ✓	very well ✓
b. Daniel	good afternoon ✓	nervous ✓
c. Juan	hello ✓	sad ✓
d. Belén	good morning ✓	calm ✓
e. Beatriz	good afternoon ✓	relaxed ✓

7. Faulty Echo

e.g. Hola, estoy muy bien.

a. Buenos días, estoy regular.

b. Estoy bien porque estoy feliz.

c. Estoy bien porque estoy relajada.

d. ¿Qué tal? Estoy fenomenal.

e. Estoy mal porque estoy triste.

f. Estoy fenomenal porque estoy tranquila.

g. Buenos días, estoy fatal.

8. Spot the Intruder

Identify the word in each sentence the speaker is NOT saying

e.g. Estoy muy bien, gracias.

a. Buenas tardes, estoy tranquilo, relajado y bien.

b. Buenos días tardes, estoy regular porque estoy triste.

c. Estoy fenomenal porque me estoy tranquila.

d. Hola, estoy un poco mal porque estoy bastante cansado.

e. ¿Cómo estás? Estoy muy bien.

9. Narrow Listening - Gap-fill

a. Hola, estoy ____________ porque estoy feliz.

b. Buenos días, estoy fenomenal porque estoy ____________________.

c. Buenas _____________, estoy mal porque estoy _________________.

d. ¿Cómo estás? Estoy muy bien, ________________.

e. Hola, __________ regular porque estoy ______________________.

f. ¿Qué tal? Estoy ___________________ pero cansada.

Unit 3. I can greet and say how I am: VOCAB BUILDING

1. Match Up

1. Cansado
2. Relajada
3. Estoy
4. Triste
5. Nerviosa
6. Tranquilo
7. Feliz
8. Contento
9. ¿Qué tal?

a. Relaxed
b. How are you?
c. Calm
d. Happy
e. Tired
f. I am
g. Cheerful
h. Nervous
i. Sad

1	
2	
3	
4	
5	
6	
7	
8	
9	

2. Broken Words

a. Regu_______ *So-so*

b. Fenome_______ *Great*

c. Fa_______ *Awful*

d. Bi_______ *Well*

e. Bue_____ dí___ *Good morning*

f. Ad_______ *Goodbye*

g. Por_______ *Because*

h. Es_______ *I am*

i. M_____ bien *Very well*

3. Complete with the missing words

a. Estoy ________ porque estoy feliz. *I am great because I am happy.*

b. ________ mal porque estoy cansada. *I am bad because I am tired.*

c. Estoy bien ________ estoy contenta. *I'm well because I am cheerful.*

d. Estoy regular porque estoy ________. *I'm so-so because I am sad.*

e. ¿Qué ______? Estoy muy bien porque estoy ____________.
How are you? I am very well because I am relaxed.

tal	estoy	fenomenal	triste	porque	relajado

Unit 3. I can greet and say how I am: READING

1. Sylla-bees
Translate the phrases putting the cells in the correct order

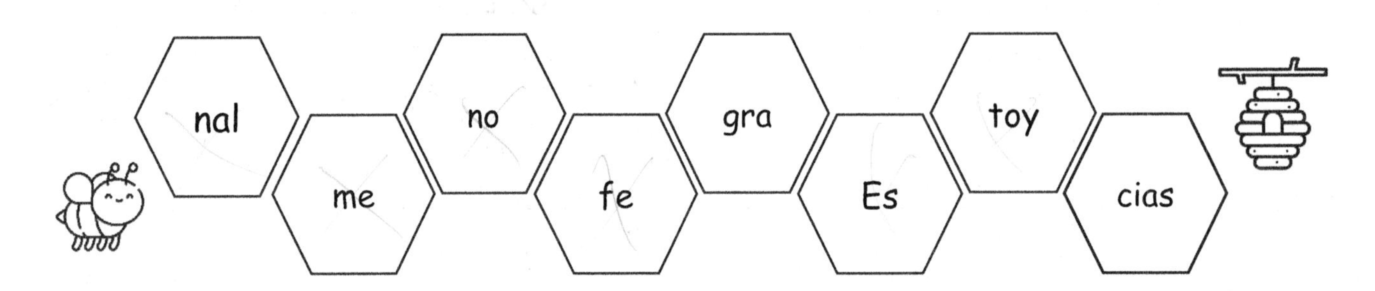

a. *I'm great, thank you.*
E________ f________________, g____________.

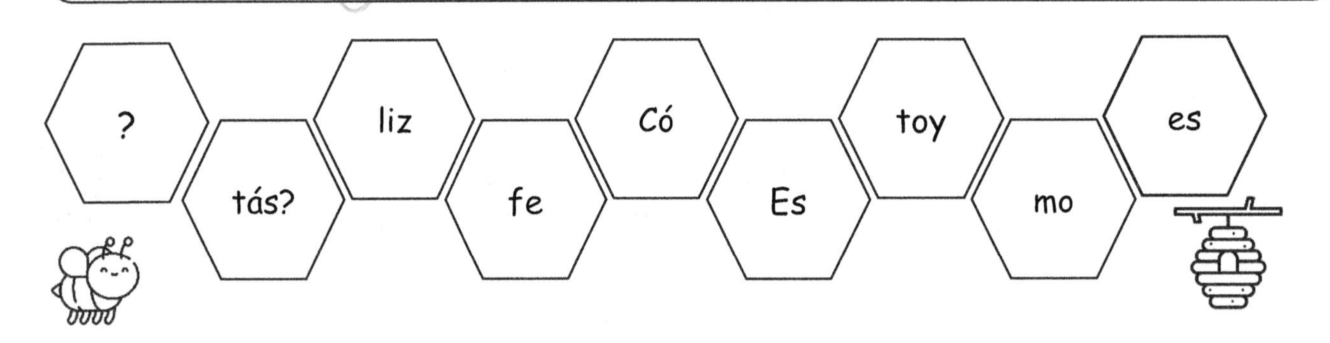

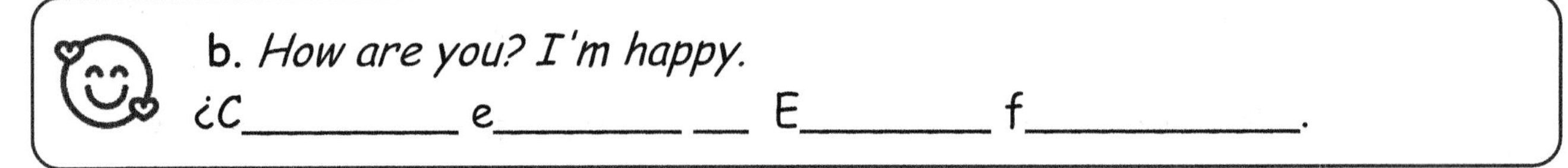

b. *How are you? I'm happy.*
¿C_________ e________ __ E________ f___________.

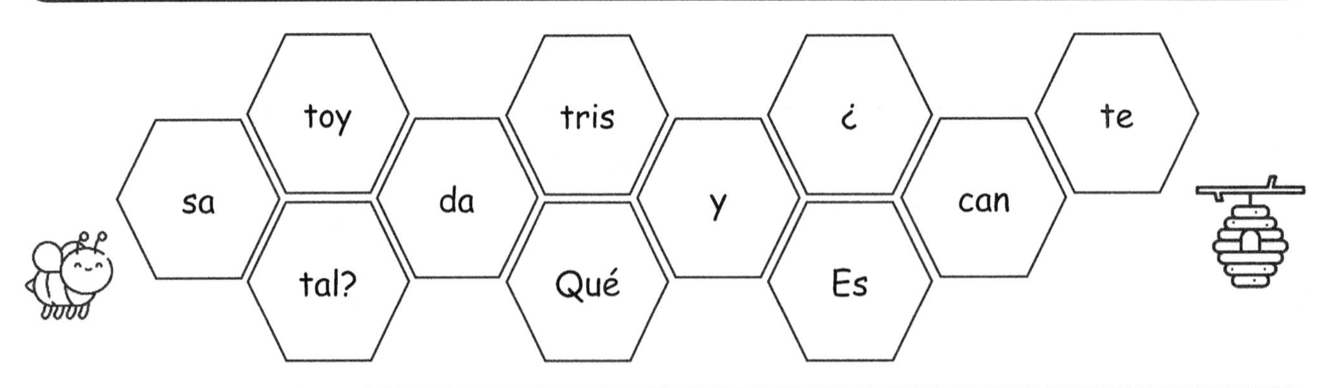

c. *How are you? I'm tired and sad (f).*
__Q______ t____? E_________ c__________ __ t____________.

2. Read the sentences and complete the grid below in English

e.g. Hola, me llamo Enrique. Tengo ocho años. Estoy muy bien porque estoy feliz.

c. Buenos días, me llamo Chari. Tengo seis años. Estoy regular porque estoy cansada.

a. Hola, me llamo Amira. Tengo once años. Estoy fenomenal porque estoy contenta.

d. Hola, me llamo Simona. Tengo nueve años. Estoy bien porque estoy tranquila.

b. Buenos días. Me llamo Mateo. Tengo trece años. Estoy bien porque estoy relajado.

e. Hola, me llamo Norberto. Tengo doce años. Estoy mal porque estoy nervioso.

	Name	Age	Feeling	Reason
e.g.	*Enrique*	*8*	*Very well*	*Happy*
a.				
b.				
c.				
d.				
e.				

Unit 3. I can greet and say how I am: WRITING

1. Spelling

a. Es ___ ___ ___ bi ___ ___. — *I am well.*

b. ___ sto ___ f ___ n ___ m ___ n ___ l. — *I am great.*

c. P ___ ___ que est ___ ___ fel ___ ___. — *Because I am happy.*

d. Porq ___ ___ estoy tr ___ ___ ___ ___. — *Because I am sad.*

e. Po ___ ___ ue ___ stoy re ___ a ___ a ___ o. — *Because I am relaxed.*

f. ¿Qu ___ t ___ ___? — *How are you?*

g. ¿ ___ óm ___ e ___ ___ ___ ___? Estoy mal. — *How are you? I am bad.*

2. Anagrams

a. toysE nvosiero. — *I am nervous.*

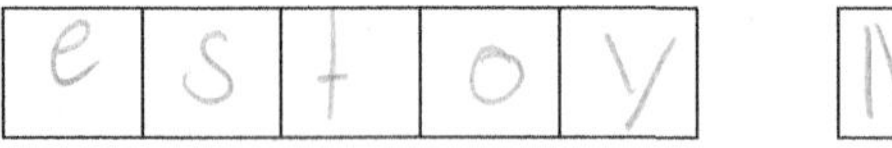

b. eM allom mónSi. — *My name is Simon.*

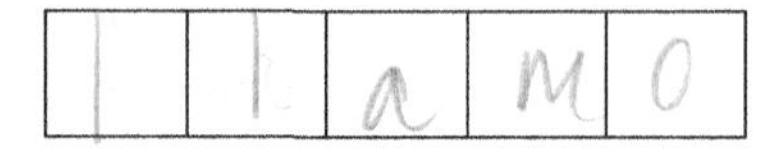

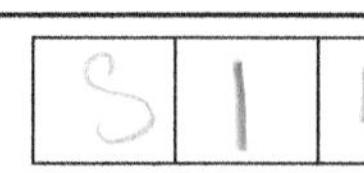

c. Etoys tresaesdo. — *I am stressed.*

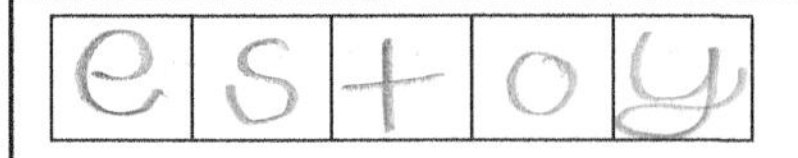

d. oN toesy zlife. — *I am not happy.*

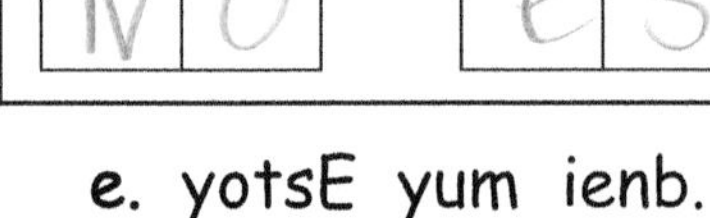

e. yotsE yum ienb. — *I am very well.*

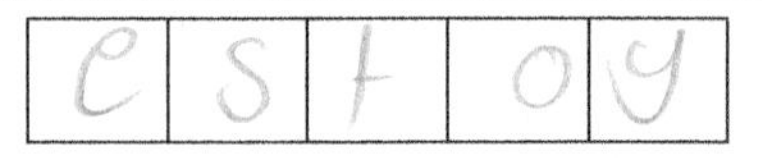

3. Faulty Translation. Spot the difference and correct with English words.

e.g. Estoy cansado.	⇒ *I am cheerful.*	*I am tired*
a. Estoy muy bien.	⇒ I am happy.	I am very happy ✓
b. ¿Cómo estás?	⇒ What's your name?	¿how are you? ✓
c. Estoy relajada.	⇒ I am nervous.	I am relaxed ✓
d. Estoy triste.	⇒ I am calm.	I am sad ✓
e. Buenos días, ¿qué tal?	⇒ Hello, how are you?	good morning, ¿how are you? ✓

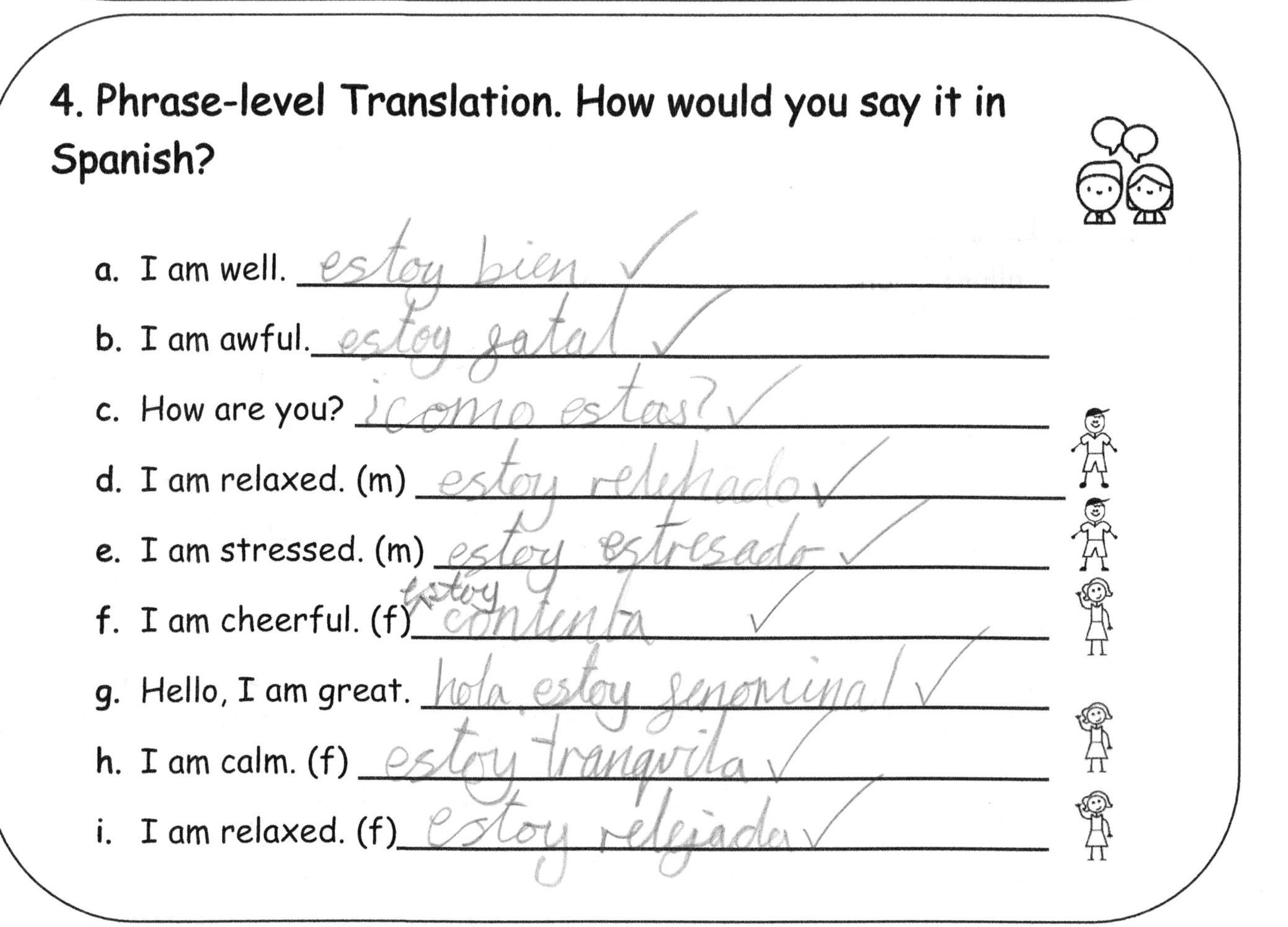

4. Phrase-level Translation. How would you say it in Spanish?

a. I am well. estoy bien ✓

b. I am awful. estoy fatal ✓

c. How are you? ¿como estas? ✓

d. I am relaxed. (m) estoy relehado ✓

e. I am stressed. (m) estoy estresado ✓

f. I am cheerful. (f) estoy contenta ✓

g. Hello, I am great. hola estoy fenominal ✓

h. I am calm. (f) estoy tranquila ✓

i. I am relaxed. (f) estoy relejiada ✓

UNIT 3 - ¿CÓMO ESTÁS?

LISTENING

1. Listen and tick the word you hear

e.g. 1 (Buenos días) a. 1 (Regular) b. 1 (Tranquilo) c. 2 (Cansado) d. 3 (Cansada) e. 3 (Feliz)

2. Listen and complete with the missing vowel

a. Estoy content**a**.
b. Buen**a**s noches.
c. Estoy tranquil**o**.
d. Buen**a**s tardes.
e. Estoy fenomenal.
f. Estoy triste.
g. Estoy cansad**o**.
h. Hola, m**e** llamo Roberto.
i. Estoy muy bien.
j. Buenos días.
k. Estoy f**a**tal.
l. Estoy relajad**o**.
m. Estoy nervios**a**.
n. Buenos días.

3. Complete with the missing syllables in the box below

a. Estoy es**tre**sado.
b. Estoy **bien**.
c. Bue**nos** días.
d. Bue**nas** tardes.
e. Estoy muy bi**en**.
f. Estoy bien por**que** estoy feliz.
g. Estoy conten**to**.
h. Hola, me **lla**mo María.
i. **Estoy** cansada.
j. Estoy mal porque estoy ner**vio**so.

4. Listen and choose the correct spelling

1\. a 2. b 3. b 4. a 5. b 6. b 7. a 8. b 9. b 10. a

5. Break the flow: Draw a line between words

a. Estoy muy bien porque estoy feliz.
b. Estoy mal porque estoy cansado.
c. Hola, estoy mal porque estoy triste.
d. ¿Qué tal? Estoy regular, gracias.
e. Hola, me llamo José y estoy bien.

6. Fill in the grid with the correct item and colour

a. Nieves ; Good morning ; Very well
b. Daniel ; Good afternoon ; Nervous
c. Juan ; Hello ; Sad.
d. Belén ; Good morning ; Calm
e. Beatriz ; Good afternoon ; Relaxed

7. Faulty Echo

e.g. Hola, estoy muy bien. (jola)
a. Buenos días, estoy regular. (reguiular con iu)
b. Estoy bien porque estoy feliz. (porque con qwue)
c. Estoy bien porque estoy relajada. (relajado con J inglesa)
d. ¿Qué tal? Estoy fenomenal. (fenomenal British accent)
e. Estoy mal porque estoy triste. (tchriste)
f. Estoy fenomenal porque estoy tranquila. (tchranquila)
g. Buenos días, estoy fatal. (feital)

8. Spot the Intruder. Identify the word in each sentence the speaker is NOT saying

a. Buenas tardes, estoy tranquilo, relajado y bien. **tranquilo**
b. Buenos días, tardes estoy regular porque estoy triste. **tardes**
c. Estoy fenomenal porque me estoy tranquila. **me**
d. Hola, estoy un poco mal porque estoy bastante cansado. **bastante**
e. ¿Cómo estás? Estoy muy bien. **muy**

9. Narrow Listening - Gap-fill

a. Hola, estoy **bien** porque estoy feliz.
b. Buenos días, estoy fenomenal porque estoy **contenta**.
c. Buenas **tardes**, estoy mal porque estoy **nervioso**.
d. ¿Cómo estás? Estoy muy bien, **gracias**.
e. Hola, **estoy** regular porque estoy **tranquilo**.
f. ¿Qué tal? Estoy **fenomenal** pero cansada.

VOCABULARY BUILDING

1. Match Up

1. e   2. a   3. f   4. i   5. h   6.c   7.d   8.g   9.b

2. Broken Words

a. Regu**lar** b. Fenome**nal** c. Fa**tal** d. **Bien** e. Bue**nos días** f. Adi**ós** g. Por**que** h. **Estoy** i. **Muy** bien

3. Complete the sentences with the words in the box below

a. Estoy **fenomenal** porque estoy feliz.
b. **Estoy** mal porque estoy cansada.
c. Estoy bien **porque** estoy contenta.
d. Estoy regular porque estoy **triste.**
e. ¿Qué **tal**? Estoy muy bien porque estoy **relajado**.

READING

1. Sylla-Bees

a. **E**stoy **f**enomenal, **g**racias .   b. **¿Cómo** e**stás**? E**stoy** f**eliz**.   c. ¿**Qué** tal? E**stoy** c**ansada** y **triste.**

2. Read the sentences and complete the grid below in English

a. Amira ; 11 ; Great ; Cheerful   c. Mateo ; 13 ; Well ; Relaxed   c. Chari ; 6 ; So-so ; Tired
d. Simona ; 9 ; Well ; Calm   e. Norberto ; 12; Bad ; Nervous

WRITING

1. Spelling

a. Est**oy** bi**en.**   b. E**stoy** fenomenal.   c. P**or**que est**oy** fel**iz.**   d. Porq**ue** estoy tr**iste.**
e. Po**r**que **e**stoy relaj**ado**.   f. ¿Qu**é** t**al**?   g. ¿C**ómo** e**stás**?

2. Anagrams

a. Estoy nervioso.   b. Me llamo Simón.   c. Estoy estresado.   d. No estoy feliz.   e. Estoy muy bien.

3. Faulty Translation

a. I am very well.   b. How are you?   c. I am relaxed.   d. I am sad.
e. Good morning, how are you?

4. Phrase-level Translation

a. Estoy bien.   b. Estoy fatal.   c. ¿Qué tal?/¿Cómo estas?   d. Estoy relajado.
e. Estoy estresado.   f. Estoy contenta.   g. Hola, estoy fenomenal.   h. Estoy tranquila.
i. Estoy relajada.

UNIT 4

MI CUMPLEAÑOS

In this unit you will learn how to say in Spanish:

- ✓ When your birthday is
- ✓ Numbers up to 31
- ✓ Months of the year

You will revisit:

- ★ Your name and age
- ★ Saying how you are

¿Cuándo es tu cumpleaños?

Mi cumpleaños es el veintiocho de marzo

UNIT 4. MI CUMPLEAÑOS

I can say when my birthday is

¿Cuándo es tu cumpleaños? *When is your birthday?*

<table>
<tr><td rowspan="2">Me llamo ......
I am called ......</td><td rowspan="2">tengo
I have</td><td>un 1*</td><td>año year</td></tr>
<tr><td>dos 2
tres 3
cuatro 4
cinco 5
seis 6
siete 7
ocho 8
nueve 9
diez 10
once 11
doce 12
trece 13
catorce 14
quince 15</td><td>años years</td></tr>
<tr><td>Mi cumpleaños es el
My birthday is on the</td><td>dieciséis 16
diecisiete 17
dieciocho 18
diecinueve 19
veinte 20
veintiuno 21
veintidós 22
veintitrés 23
veinticuatro 24
veinticinco 25
veintiséis 26
veintisiete 27
veintiocho 28
veintinueve 29
treinta 30
treinta y uno 31</td><td>de</td><td>enero January
febrero February
marzo March
abril April
mayo May
junio June
julio July
agosto August
septiembre September
octubre October
noviembre November
diciembre December</td></tr>
</table>

Author's note: *the number "uno" becomes "un" when it comes before a noun.*

e.g. Tengo un año.

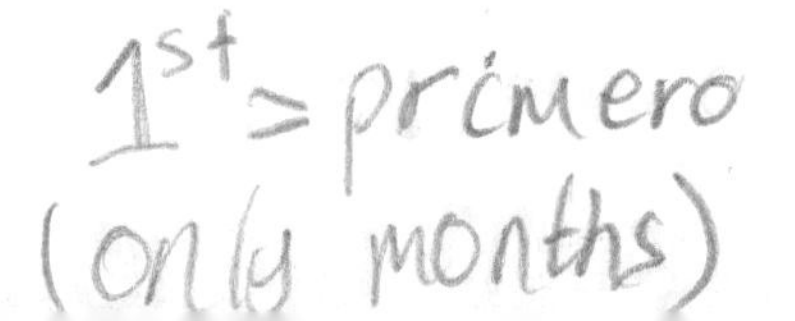

Unit 4. I can say when my birthday is: LISTENING

1. Listen and tick the word you hear

	a	b	c
1.	Seis	Siete	Tres
2.	Junio	Julio	Uno
3.	Dieciséis	Diecisiete	Dieciocho
4.	Veintidós	Veinticuatro	Veintinueve
5.	Septiembre	Noviembre	Diciembre
6.	Años	Cumpleaños	Año

2. Faulty Echo

e.g. Tengo seis años.

a. Mi cumpleaños es...

b. El diecinueve de abril.

c. Me llamo Nacho.

d. El veintiséis de junio.

e. El dieciocho de octubre.

f. Tengo once años.

g. El dieciséis de diciembre.

h. El trece de marzo.

3. Listen and complete with the missing letters

a. El do__e de ma__o.

b. El __atorce de febre__o.

c. El tre__ de __ulio.

d. El veint__séis de ju__io.

e. El ve__nte de septi__mbre.

f. El q__ince de o__tubre.

g. Tengo oc__o añ__s.

h. El tr__inta d__ enero.

4. Complete with the missing syllables in the box below

a. Tengo di __ __ años.

b. El veintio __ __ __ de septiembre.

c. El treinta y uno de __ __ lio.

d. Mi __ __ __ pleaños es...

e. El die __ __ siete de agosto.

f. El doce de ju __ __ __.

g. El __ __ __ tro de marzo.

h. El tres de e __ __ ro.

i. El __ __ __ __ ticinco de mayo.

j. El __ __ __ __ __ ta de abril.

cua	cum	ci	ju	vein	cho	ne	trein	ez	nio

5. Can you help the penguin to break the flow?

6. Fill in the grid with the correct date of birth

	Day	Month
e.g.	*12th*	*April*
a.	15th ✓	January ✓
b.	18th ✓	September ✓
c.	24th ✓	October ✓
d.	27th ✓	November ✓
e.	5 ✓	June ✓

7. Spot the Intruder

Identify the word in each sentence the speaker is NOT saying

e.g. Mi cumpleaños es <u>*tres*</u> *el diez de diciembre.*

a. Mi cumpleaños es el diecinueve de no septiembre.

b. Mi cumpleaños es me el veinte de enero.

c. ¿Cuándo tengo es tu cumpleaños?

d. Me llamo Pedro. Mi cumpleaños es el años dos de febrero.

e. Mi cumpleaños es el quince de llamo junio.

f. Mi noviembre cumpleaños es el treinta y uno de octubre.

8. Catch it, Swap it: rewrite the wrong word

e.g. Mi cumpleaños es el cuatro de enero.	agosto
a. Tengo doce años. Mi cumpleaños es el diez de marzo.	trece ✓
b. Tengo tres años. Mi cumpleaños es el veinte de julio.	diez ✓
c. Mi cumpleaños es el treinta y uno de octubre.	veintiuno ✓
d. Tengo once años. ¿Cuándo es tu cumpleaños?	doce ✓
e. Me llamo Sergio. Mi cumpleaños es el trece de abril.	tres ✓
f. Me llamo Pilar. Mi cumpleaños es el cuatro de agosto.	Junio ✓
g. Me llamo Antonio. Mi cumpleaños es el seis de julio.	octubre ✓

14/14

9. Listen, Tick or Cross

	✓	✗
e.g. David's birthday is the 9th December.	✓	
a. Pedro is 13 years old.		
b. Marta's birthday is the 7th June.		
c. Pilar is 15 years old. Her birthday is the 8th May.		
d. Antonio's birthday is on the 17th November.		
e. Dylan's birthday is the 18th October.		
f. Gianfranco's birthday is on the 15th July.		

Unit 4. I can say when my birthday is: READING

1. Sylla-Bees
   Translate the phrases putting the cells in the correct order

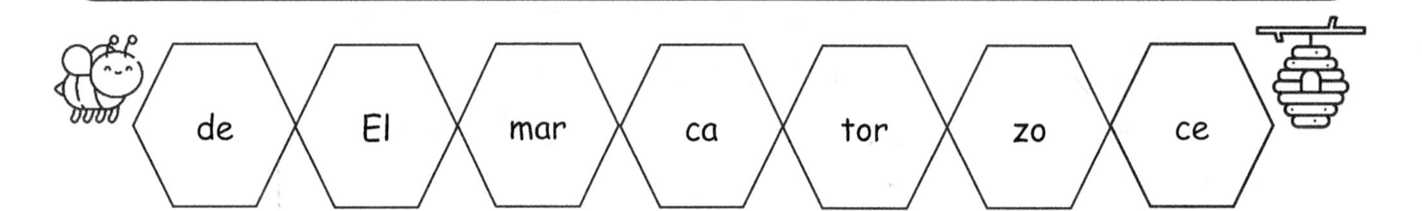

a. *The 14th of March.*
E__ c__________ d___ m__________ .

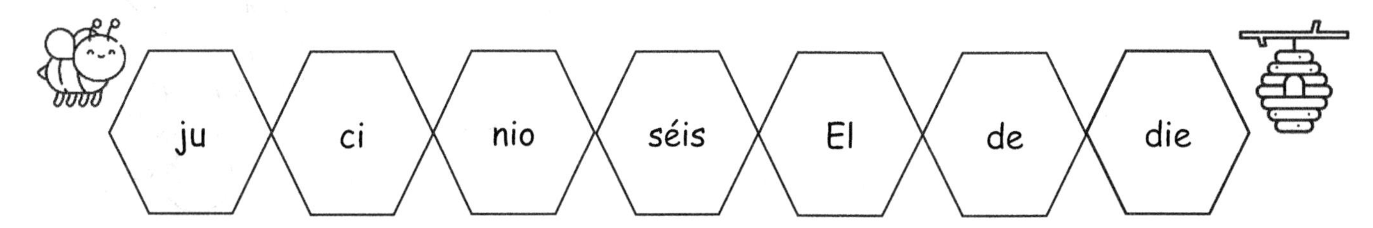

b. *The 16th of June.*
E__ d______________ d__ j________.

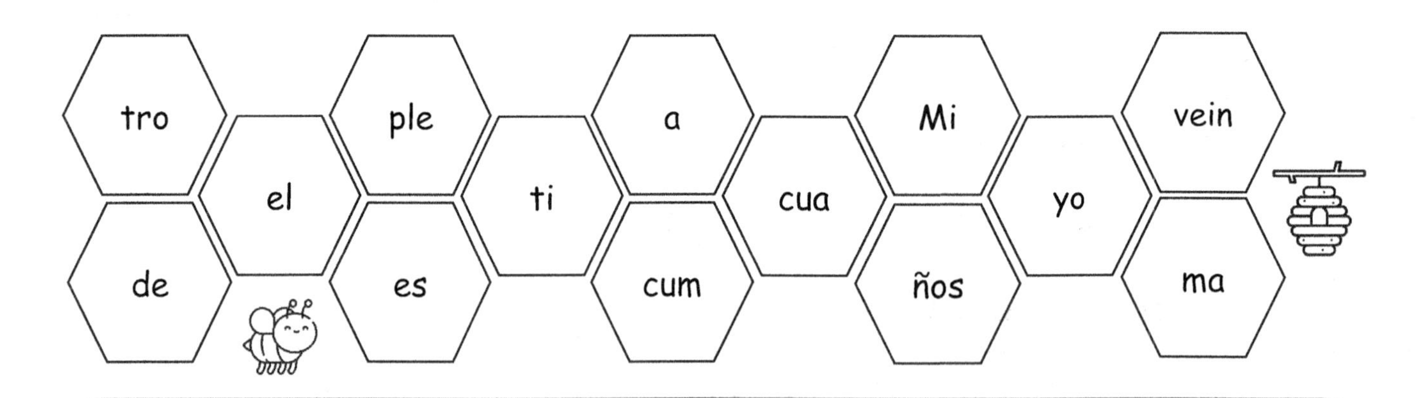

c. *My birthday is on the 24th of May.*
M___ c______________ e__ e__ v____________ d__ m_____.

2. True or False

Read the paragraphs below and then answer True or False

1. Hola, me llamo Sara García Sánchez. Estoy muy bien porque estoy feliz. Tengo siete años. Mi cumpleaños es el diecinueve de septiembre.

2. Hola, me llamo Ricardo González Gómez. Estoy fatal porque estoy cansado. Tengo diez años. Mi cumpleaños es el veintiuno de abril.

	True	False
1 **a.** Her name is **Sara.**		
b. She is great because she is happy.		
c. She is 6 years old.		
d. Her birthday is on the 13th of October.		
2 **a.** His name is **Francisco.**		
b. He is awful because he is nervous.		
c. He is 10 years old.		
d. His birthday is on the 22nd April.		

3. Tick or Cross

A. Put a tick if you find the words in the text or a cross if you do not find them.

Hola, me llamo **Ariella**. Estoy bien porque estoy tranquila. Tengo siete años. Mi cumpleaños es el catorce de febrero.

	✓	✕
a. Me llamo		
b. Doce años		
c. Hola		
d. Estoy mal		
e. Mi cumpleaños es		
f. El siete de febrero		

Hola, me llamo **Lenny**. Estoy fatal porque estoy triste. Tengo nueve años. Mi cumpleaños es el veinticuatro de julio.

	✓	✕
g. I am 7 years old		
h. My birthday		
i. 24th July		
j. Because I am happy		
k. I am stressed		

B. Find the Spanish in the texts above

a. My name is ____________________

b. My birthday is ____________________

c. I am 7 years old ____________________

d. ...because I am calm (f)____________________

4. Language Detective

- Me llamo **Pedro** González Ortega. Estoy muy bien porque estoy feliz. Tengo doce años. Mi cumpleaños es el dieciocho de febrero.

- Buenas tardes. Me llamo **Verónica** María de León. Estoy mal porque estoy estresada. Tengo trece años. Mi cumpleaños es el cuatro de agosto.

- Hola, soy **Carlos** Martín Ramos. Estoy fenomenal porque estoy contento. Tengo catorce años. Mi cumpleaños es el once de julio.

- Buenos días. Me llamo **Francisco** Ramón Morales. Estoy regular porque estoy cansado. Tengo diez años. Mi cumpleaños es el treinta de octubre.

A. Find someone who...

a. ...is 12 years old.

b. ...is tired.

c. ...is happy.

d. ...was born on the 11th July.

e. ...is 13 years old.

f. ...is cheerful.

g. ...was born on the 18th February.

B. Put a cross in the box and underline the corresponding Spanish translation. One is odd.

My name is	I am 14 years old	I am bad
Good morning	My birthday	Hello, I am
because I am stressed	I am so-so	30th October
I am great	Good afternoon	I am 11 years old

Unit 4. I can say when my birthday is: WRITING

1. Spelling

a. B__ __no__ d__ __s.	*Good morning.*
b. M__ c__ __ __lea__ __ __.	*My birthday.*
c. El t__ e__ de no__ __em__ __e.	*The 3rd of November.*
d. __l __ __nco de ab__ __l.	*The 5th of April.*
e. El tr__ __ __ de en__r__.	*The 13th of January.*
f. El q__ __nce d__ j__ __io.	*The 15th of July.*
g. Te__ __o s__ __s a__o__.	*I am 6 years old.*

2. Anagrams

a. ieSte de tuocrbe — *7th of October.*

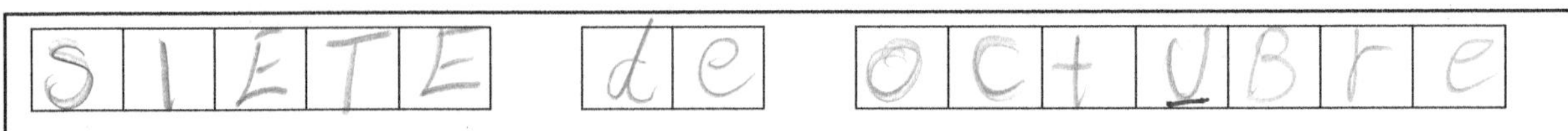

b. ctoerCa ed gostao — *14th of August.*

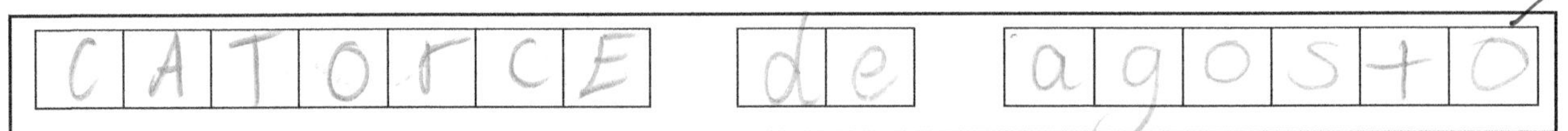

c. ceOn ed ciebemdir — *11th of December.*

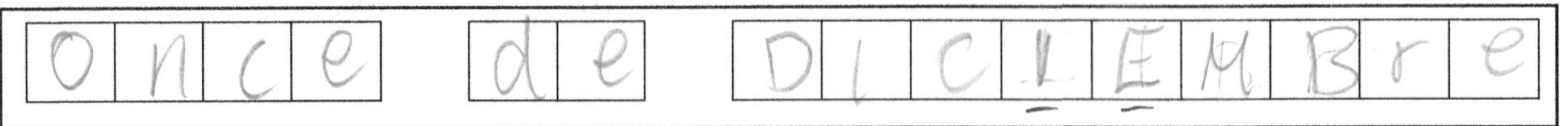

d. retiTan de nijou — *30th of June.*

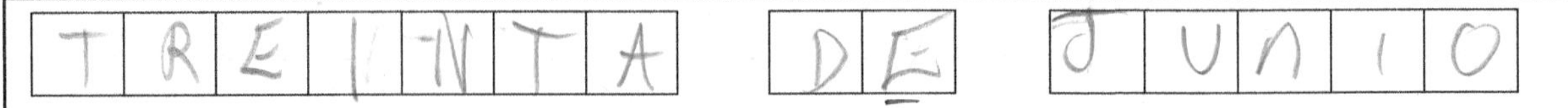

3. Gapped Translation

Complete the translation

a. Tengo siete años.	*I am* 7 *years old.*
b. Tengo seis años.	*I am* 6 *years old.*
c. No estoy cansado.	*I am not* tired.
d. Estoy feliz.	*I am* happy.
e. El dieciséis de febrero.	*The* 16th *of February.*
f. El veintitrés de agosto.	*The* 23rd *of August.*
g. Buenas tardes.	*Good* afternoon.

4. Split Sentences

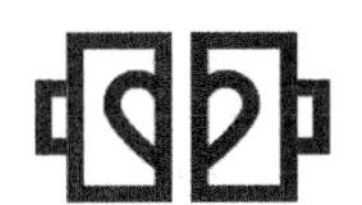

a. Me llamo	1. el doce de abril.
b. Estoy	2. once años.
c. Tengo	3. Pedro García López.
d. Mi cumpleaños es	4. estoy cansado.
e. Estoy regular porque	5. tu cumpleaños?
f. ¿Cuándo es	6. muy bien.

a	b	c	d	e	f
3	6	2	1	4	5

5. Rock Climbing

Starting from the bottom, pick one chunk from each row to translate the sentences below.

de enero.	veintitrés de junio.	Tengo diez años.	de julio.	el tres de mayo.
cumpleaños es el	el cinco	Mi cumpleaños es	de marzo.	Es el quince
el veintiocho	Francisco.	cumpleaños?	años. Mi	Mi cumpleaños es
Me llamo	Tengo doce	Mi cumpleaños es	Tengo once años.	¿Cuándo es tu
a.	b.	c.	d.	e.

a. My name is Francisco. My birthday is on the 3rd May.

____

b. I am 12 years old. My birthday is on the 23rd of June.

____

c. My birthday is on the 28th March. I am 10 years old.

____

d. I am 11 years old. My birthday is on the 5th of July.

____

e. When is your birthday? It's on the 15th of January.

____

6. Mosaic Translation

Use the words in the grid to help you translate the sentences below.

a.	Tengo trece	Mi cumpleaños	Tengo	veintidós de	diciembre.
b.	¿Cuántos	años. Mi	es el	de	once años.
c.	Me llamo Ana.	es el treinta y uno	Es el dieciséis	Tengo	abril.
d.	¿Cuándo es	años tienes?	cumpleaños es el	doce	agosto.
e.	Mi cumpleaños	tu cumpleaños?	de octubre.	dieciocho de	años.

a. I am 13 years old. My birthday is on the 18th of April.

Tengo trece. Mi cumpleaños es el Veintidós de abril. ✓

b. How old are you? I am 12 years old.

¿Cuántos años tienes? Tengo doce años. ✓

c. My name is Ana. My birthday is on the 22th of August.

Me llamo Ana. Mi cumpleaños dieciocho de agosto. ✓

d. When is your birthday? It's on the 16th of December.

¿Cuandos es tu cumpleanos? es el dieciséis diciembre. ✓

e. My birthday is on the 31st of October. I am 11 years old.

Mi cumpleanos es el treinta y uno de octubre.

7. Sentence Puzzle

Put the words in the correct order

a. es de cumpleaños Mi el septiembre trece

b. ¿tu Cuándo cumpleaños es?

c. abril de Mi cumpleaños el es doce

d. llamo Me Carlos nueve y tengo años

e. de Mi enero cumpleaños el diecinueve es

f. el de diciembre Mi es cumpleaños veinticuatro

g. llamo Me Chari tengo años catorce y

h. llamo María el es doce enero de Me cumpleaños y mi

i. ¿Cuántos Tengo años años siete tienes?

8. Tangled Translation

a. Write the Spanish words in English to complete the translation

Hello, **me llamo Felipe**. **Estoy** very well **porque estoy** happy. **Tengo** ten **años**.

Mi cumpleaños is **el veinte** of January. When is **tu cumpleaños**?

b. Write the English words in Spanish to complete the translation

Hola, **my name is** Jimena. **I am** mal **because** estoy **tired**. **I am** once **years old**.

My birthday es el ocho **of** julio. ¿Cuándo es **your birthday**?

9. Fill in the Gaps

a. Hola, me __________ Alejandro. Estoy __________ porque __________ contento. Tengo catorce __________. Mi cumpleaños es el __________ de octubre.

bien	quince	años	llamo	estoy

b. Hola, me llamo Rubén. __________ nueve años. Estoy mal __________ estoy __________. Mi cumpleaños ____ el veintidós de __________.

triste	es	tengo	febrero	porque

10. Guided Translation

a. M__ ll______ S__________ y t________ o_______ a_______.

My name is Simona and I am 11 years old.

b. E_______ m____ b______ p________ e________ c___________.

I am very well because I am cheerful. (m)

c. N__ e_______ b_____ p________ e________ c____________.

I am not well because I am tired. (f)

d. M___ c______________ e___ e___ q__________ d___ a__________.

My birthday is on the 15th of August.

e. ¿C__________ e___ t___ c__________________?

When is your birthday?

11. Pyramid Translation

Translate into Spanish starting from the top. Write the sentences in the grid below.

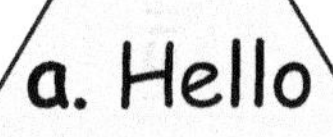

a. Hello

b. Hello, my name is Juan.

c. Hello, my name is Juan. I am 10 years old.

d. Hello, my name is Juan. I am 10 years old. My birthday is

e. Hello, my name is Juan. I am 10 years old. My birthday is on the 24th of October.

a.
b.
c.
d.
e.

No Snakes No Ladders

SALIDA	1 Me llamo Juan	2 Tengo doce años	3 Hola ¿qué tal?	4 Estoy muy bien	5 Estoy regular	6 Porque estoy cansado	7 ¿Cómo te llamas?
15 Mi cumplea-ños es	14 Pero estoy nerviosa	13 Porque estoy relajada	12 Estoy fenome-nal	11 Tengo doce años	10 ¿Cuántos años tienes?	9 Estoy feliz	8 Estoy un poco estresado
16 El veinte de mayo	17 El once de junio	18 ¿Cuándo es tu cumplea-ños?	19 No estoy triste	20 Estoy mal	21 El treinta y uno de octubre	22 Tengo nueve años	23 Gracias
LLEGADA	30 Buenas tardes, estoy fatal	29 Estoy contento	28 Tengo quince años	27 El treinta de enero	26 Porque estoy tranquila	25 Buenos días, estoy regular	24 El veintiséis de julio

Unit 3-4

No Snakes No Ladders

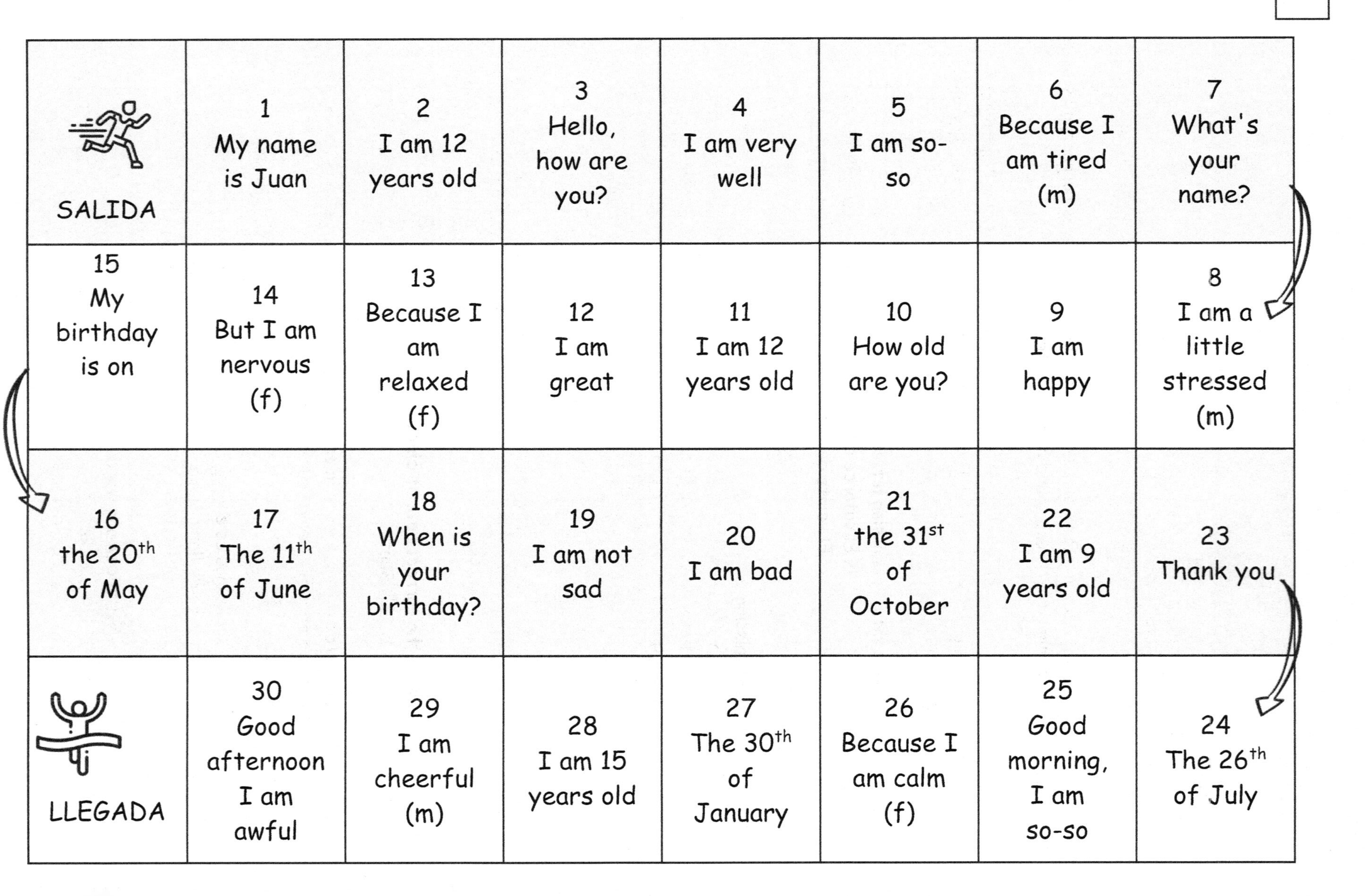

SALIDA	1 My name is Juan	2 I am 12 years old	3 Hello, how are you?	4 I am very well	5 I am so-so	6 Because I am tired (m)	7 What's your name?
15 My birthday is on	14 But I am nervous (f)	13 Because I am relaxed (f)	12 I am great	11 I am 12 years old	10 How old are you?	9 I am happy	8 I am a little stressed (m)
16 the 20th of May	17 The 11th of June	18 When is your birthday?	19 I am not sad	20 I am bad	21 the 31st of October	22 I am 9 years old	23 Thank you
LLEGADA	30 Good afternoon I am awful	29 I am cheerful (m)	28 I am 15 years old	27 The 30th of January	26 Because I am calm (f)	25 Good morning, I am so-so	24 The 26th of July

UNIT 4 - MI CUMPLEAÑOS

LISTENING

1. Listen and tick the word you hear

1. c 2. b 3. a 4. b 5. c 6. b

2. Faulty Echo. You will listen to the sentence twice. The first one is correct, and the second one has an incorrect sound. Underline the wrong sound in each sentence.

e.g. *Tengo seis años.*

a. Mi cumpleaños es...
b. ...el diecinueve de abril
c. Me llamo Nacho.
d. ...el veintiséis de junio
e. ...el dieciocho de octubre
f. Tengo once años.
g. ...el dieciséis de diciembre
h. ...el trece de marzo

3. Listen and complete with the missing letters

a. El doce de mayo
b. El **c**atorce de febrer**o**
c. El tre**s** de julio
d. El veintiséis de junio
e. El veinte de septi**e**mbre
f. El quince de octubre
g. Tengo ocho añ**os**.
h. El treinta d**e** enero

4. Complete with the missing syllables in the box below

a. Tengo di**ez** años.
b. El veinti**ocho** de septiembre
c. El treinta y uno de **ju**lio
d. Mi **cum**pleaños es...
e. El dieci**si**ete de agosto
f. El doce de ju**nio**
g. El **cua**tro de marzo
h. El tres de **e**ne**ro**
i. El **vein**ticinco de mayo
j. El **trein**ta de abril

5. Break the flow:

a. Mi cumpleaños es el diecisiete de noviembre.
b. Me llamo María. Tengo once años.
c. Mi cumpleaños es el cuatro de agosto.
d. ¿Cuándo es tu cumpleaños? El dos de abril.
e. Mi cumpleaños es el veintidós de mayo.
f. Mi cumpleaños es el trece de febrero.

6. Fill in the grid with the correct date of birth

a. 15th Jan b. 18th Sept c. 24th Oct d. 27th Nov e. 5th June

7. Spot the Intruder. Identify the word in each sentence the speaker is NOT saying

a. Mi cumpleaños es el diecinueve de no septiembre. **no**
b. Mi cumpleaños es me el veinte de enero. **me**
c. ¿Cuándo tengo es tu cumpleaños? **tengo**
d. Me llamo Pedro. Mi cumpleaños es el años dos de febrero. **años**
e. Mi cumpleaños es el quince de llamo junio. **llamo**
f. Mi noviembre cumpleaños es el treinta y uno de octubre. **noviembre**

8. Catch it, Swap it: rewrite the wrong word

a. Tengo **trece** años.
b. ...tengo **diez** años
c. ...el **veintiuno** de octubre
d. Tengo **doce** años...
e. ...el **tres** de abril
f. ...el cuatro de **junio**
g. ...el seis de **octubre**

9. Listen, Tick or Cross

a. X (12 years old) b. ✓ c. X (13 years old, 7th June) d. ✓ e. ✓ f. X (15th June)

READING

1. Sylla-bees

a. El catorce de marzo b. El dieciséis de junio c. Mi cumpleaños es el veinticuatro de mayo.

2. True or False

1a. True b. False (very well) c. False (7) d. False (19th of September)
2a. False (Francisco) b. False (tired) c. True d. False (22nd of April)

3A. Tick or Cross

a. ✓ b. X c. ✓ d. X e. ✓ f. X
g. X h. ✓ i. ✓ j. X k. X

3B. Find the Spanish in the text above

a. Me llamo... b. Mi cumpleaños es... c. Tengo siete años. d. Porque estoy tranquila.

4. Language Detective

A. Find someone who...

a . Pedro b. Francisco c. Pedro d. Carlos e. Verónica f. Carlo g. Pedro

B. Odd one out: I am 11 years old. (odd chunk)

WRITING

1. Spelling

a. Buenos días. b. Mi cumpleaños c. El tres de noviembre d. El cinco de abril
e. El trece de enero f. El quince de junio g. Tengo seis años.

2. Anagrams

a. Siete de octubre b. Catorce de agosto c. Once de diciembre d. Treinta de junio

3. Gapped Translation

a. I am **seven** years old. b. I am **six** years old. c. I am not **tired**. d. I am **happy.**
e. The **16th** of February f. The **23rd** of August g. Good **afternoon/evening.**

4. Split Sentences

a. 3 b. 6 c. 2 d. 1 e. 4 f. 5

5. Rock Climbing

a. Me llamo Francisco. Mi cumpleaños es el tres de mayo.
b. Tengo doce años. Mi cumpleaños es el veintitrés de junio.
c. Mi cumpleaños es el veintiocho de marzo. Tengo diez años.
d. Tengo once años. Mi cumpleaños es el cinco de julio.
e. ¿Cuándo es tu cumpleaños? Es el quince de enero.

6. Mosaic Translation

a. Tengo trece años. Mi cumpleaños es el dieciocho de abril.
b. ¿Cuántos años tienes? Tengo doce años.
c. Me llamo Ana. Mi cumpleaños es el veintidós de agosto.
d. ¿Cuándo es tu cumpleaños? Es el dieciséis de diciembre.
e. Mi cumpleaños es el treinta y uno de octubre. Tengo once años.

7. Sentence Puzzle

a. Mi cumpleaños es el trece de septiembre.
b. ¿Cuándo es tu cumpleaños?
c. Mi cumpleaños es el doce de abril.
d. Me llamo Carlos y tengo nueve años.
e. Mi cumpleaños es el diecinueve de enero.
f. Mi cumpleaños es el veinticuatro de diciembre.
g. Me llamo Chari y tengo catorce años.
h. Me llamo María y mi cumpleaños es el doce de enero.
i. ¿Cuántos años tienes? Tengo siete años.

8. Tangled Translation

a. Hello, **my name is** Felipe. **I am** very well **because I am** happy. **I am** ten **years old**. **My birthday** is **on the 20th** of January. When is **your birthday?**

b. Hola, **me llamo** Jimena. **Estoy** mal **porque** estoy **cansada. Tengo** once **años**. **Mi cumpleaños** es el ocho **de** julio. ¿Cuándo es **tu cumpleaños?**

9. Fill in the Gaps

a. Hola, me **llamo** Alejandro. Estoy **bien** porque **estoy** contento. Tengo catorce **años**. Mi cumpleaños es el **quince** de octubre.

b. Hola, me llamo Rubén. **Tengo** nueve años. Estoy mal **porque** estoy **triste**. Mi cumpleaños **es** el veintidós de **febrero**.

10. Guided Translation

a. **Me** llamo **Simona** y **tengo** once **años.**
b. **Estoy** muy **bien porque estoy** contento.
c. No **estoy** bien **porque estoy cansada.**
d. Mi **cumpleaños es el quince** de **agosto.**
e. **¿Cuándo es** tu **cumpleaños**?

11. Pyramid Translation

Hola, me llamo Juan. Tengo diez años. Mi cumpleaños es el veinticuatro de octubre.

UNIT 5
MI MASCOTA

In this unit you will learn how to say in Spanish:

- ✓ What pets you have at home
- ✓ What colour are your pets
- ✓ What their name is
- ✓ *Tengo/tienes*
- ✓ *No tengo/no tienes*

You will revisit:

- ★ Saying your name
- ★ How to say your age and birthday

Tengo un perro

Tengo un gato

UNIT 5. MI MASCOTA

I can say what pets I have

¿Tienes una mascota? *Do you have a pet?*

<table>
<tr>
<td>Yo
I</td>
<td>tengo
I have

no tengo
I do not have</td>
<td rowspan="2">un
a</td>
<td rowspan="2">caballo horse
conejo rabbit
gato cat
hámster hamster
loro parrot
pájaro bird
perro dog
pez fish
pingüino penguin
ratón mouse</td>
<td rowspan="2">amarillo yellow
blanco white
negro black
rojo red

azul blue
gris grey
marrón brown
rosa pink
verde green
grande big
pequeño small</td>
<td rowspan="4">que se llama
which is called

y
and

pero
but</td>
<td rowspan="4">Coco
Dida
Lola
Maya
Pablo
Pepe
Rocky
Zar</td>
</tr>
<tr>
<td rowspan="2">Tú
You</td>
<td rowspan="2">tienes
you have

no tienes
you do not have</td>
</tr>
<tr>
<td>una
a</td>
<td>araña spider
cobaya guinea pig
gallina chicken
oveja sheep
tortuga tortoise/turtle</td>
<td rowspan="2">amarilla yellow
blanca white
negra black
roja red

azul blue
gris grey
marrón brown
rosa pink
verde green
grande big
pequeña small</td>
</tr>
<tr>
<td colspan="4">No tengo mascotas
I don't have pets</td>
</tr>
</table>

Me gustría - I would like

Unit 5. I can say what pets I have: LISTENING

1. Listen and complete with the missing vowel

a. Un p__rro

b. Un cab__llo

c. Un gat__

d. Un p__z

e. Una tort__ga

f. Una ov__ja

g. Un con__jo

h. Una gall__na

2. Listen and tick the word you hear

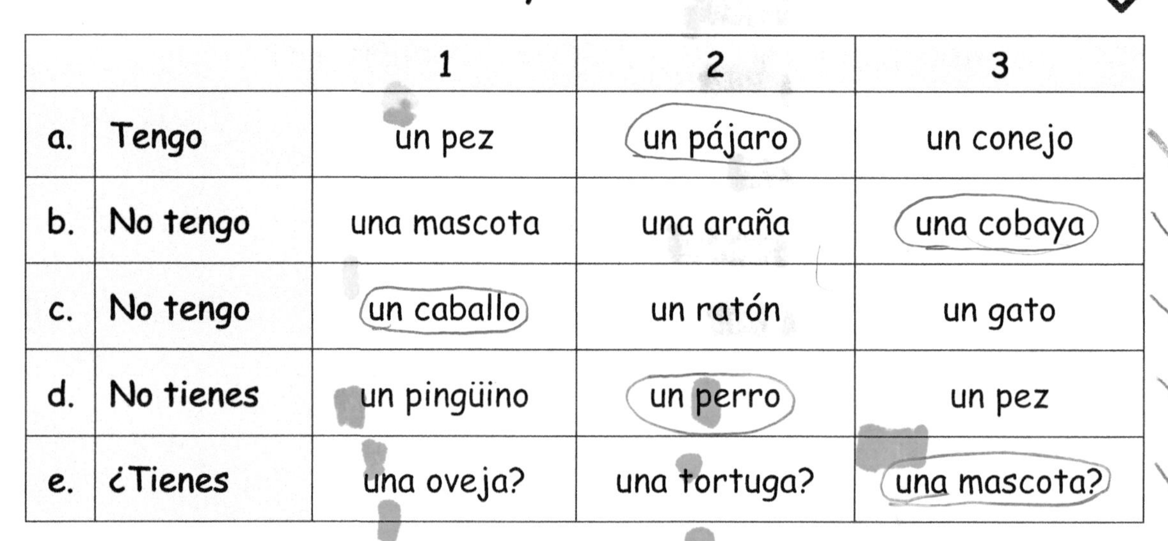

		1	2	3
a.	Tengo	un pez	un pájaro	un conejo
b.	No tengo	una mascota	una araña	una cobaya
c.	No tengo	un caballo	un ratón	un gato
d.	No tienes	un pingüino	un perro	un pez
e.	¿Tienes	una oveja?	una tortuga?	una mascota?

3. Complete with the missing syllables in the box below

a. Un perro ne _ _ _.

b. Una _ _ llina blanca.

c. Un ca _ _ llo gris.

d. Un pez a _ _ _.

e. Un cone _ _ marrón.

f. Una a _ _ ña negra.

g. Una oveja ro _ _.

h. Un loro amari _ _ _ .

4. Complete the words with the missing endings

a. Un pájar_o_ amarill_o_.

b. Una ovej_a_ ros_a_.

c. Un lor_o_ roj_o_.

d. Un gat_o_ negr_o_.

e. Una tortug_a_ naranj_a_.

f. Un perr_o_ blanc_o_.

g. Un pingüin_o_ pequeñ_o_.

h. Una gallin_a_ negr_a_.

i. Un pe_z_ verd_e_.

j. Una cobay_a_ blanc_a_.

5. Write the missing word as you hear it.

a. Un ___pájaro___ azul.

b. Una ___araña___ amarilla.

c. Un ___conejo___ rosa.

d. Un ___pingüino___ negro.

e. Una ___cobaya___ blanca.

f. Una ___obeja___ roja.

g. Un perro ___marrón___.

h. Un ratón ___pequeño___.

i. Una ___gallina___ grande.

j. Tengo un ___loro___.

k. ___no___ tengo un gato.

6. Faulty Echo

Underline the wrong word

a. No tengo un pingüino gris.

b. Tengo una oveja rosa.

c. No tienes un pez azul.

d. No tengo un gato pequeño.

e. Tienes una gallina pequeña.

f. No tienes un caballo marrón.

g. No tengo mascotas.

h. Tengo una tortuga verde.

i. Tengo un loro amarillo.

j. No tengo una araña roja.

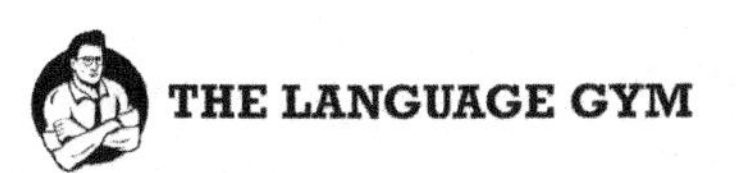

7. Listen and choose the correct spelling

	1	2
a.	Me lamo	Me llamo
b.	Años	Anos
c.	Huan	Juan
d.	Conexo	Conejo
e.	Espanol	Español
f.	Cinco	Sinco
g.	Amarillo	Amarilo
h.	Ojo	Ocho
i.	Patricia	Patricha
j.	Cabayo	Caballo
k.	Oveja	Oveha
l.	Naranga	Naranja

8. Fill in the grid with the correct information in English

	Pet	Colour
a.		
b.		
c.		
d.		
e.		
f.		

9. Spot the Intruder

Identify the word in each sentence the speaker is NOT saying

a. Tengo un pez azul y un dos gato gris.

b. ¿Tienes un mascotas? No, no tengo mascotas.

c. Tú tienes un caballo blanco que como se llama Rocky.

d. Yo tengo un perro marrón y no grande.

e. Tú no tienes una araña grande, pero tienes un ratón pequeño.

f. Yo tengo un pingüino gris blanco que se llama Pepe.

10. Catch it, Swap it

Listen, spot the difference between what you hear and the written text and edit each sentence accordingly

e.g. Tengo un gato marrón y blanco.	*conejo*
a. Tienes un caballo grande y gris.	
b. No tengo una gallina negra y amarilla.	
c. Tengo un conejo, pero no tengo una oveja.	
d. No tienes un pez azul, pero tienes una araña.	
e. ¿Tienes una mascota? Sí, tengo un perro negro.	
f. No tengo un pingüino, pero tengo una cobaya.	
g. Tengo un loro pequeño que se llama Rocky.	

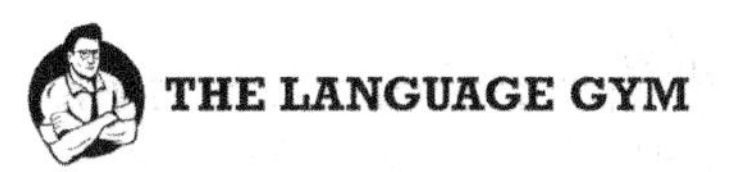

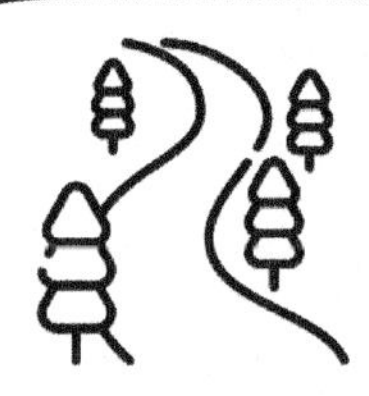

11. Listening Slalom

Listen and pick the equivalent English words from each column - drawing a line as you follow the speaker

e.g. Tengo un gato negro - I have a black cat

You could colour in the boxes for each sentence in a different colour and read out the sentence in Spanish

e.g.	***I have***		blue
a.	You have		***black***
b.	I don't have		pink
c.	I have		white
d.	You do not have		brown
e.	I have		grey
f.	I don't have		yellow

Unit 5. I can say what pets I have: READING

1. Sylla-Bees

Read and put the syllables in the cells in the correct order

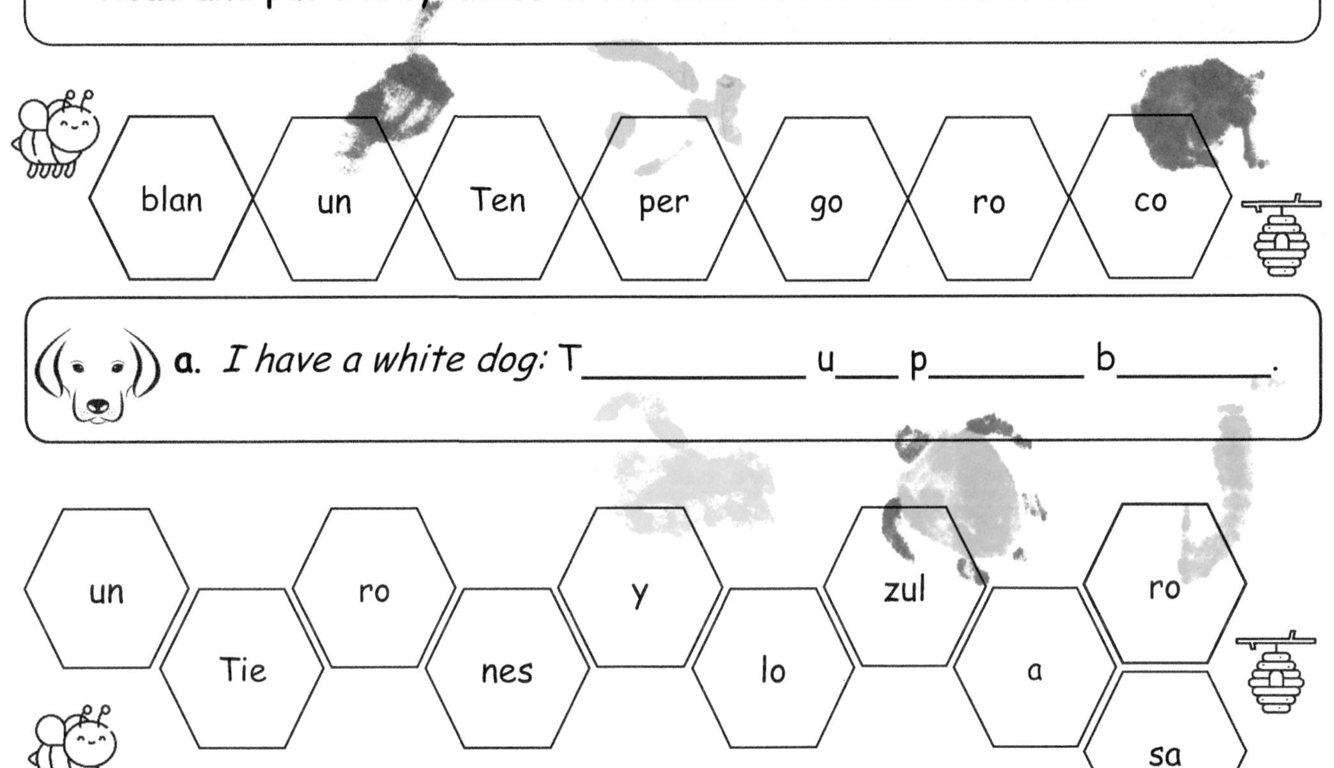

a. *I have a white dog:* T__________ u___ p________ b________.

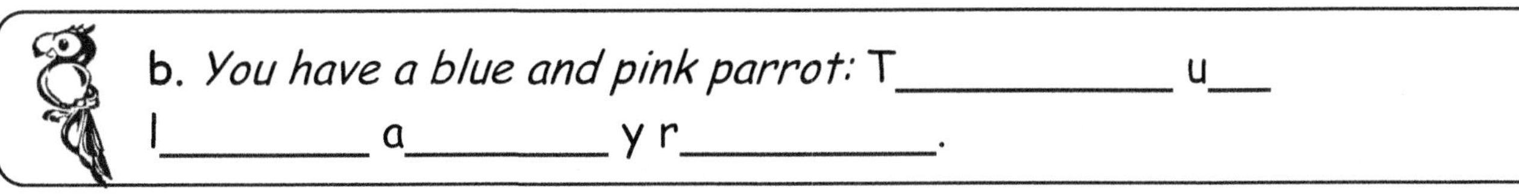

b. *You have a blue and pink parrot:* T___________ u__ l_________ a_________ y r___________.

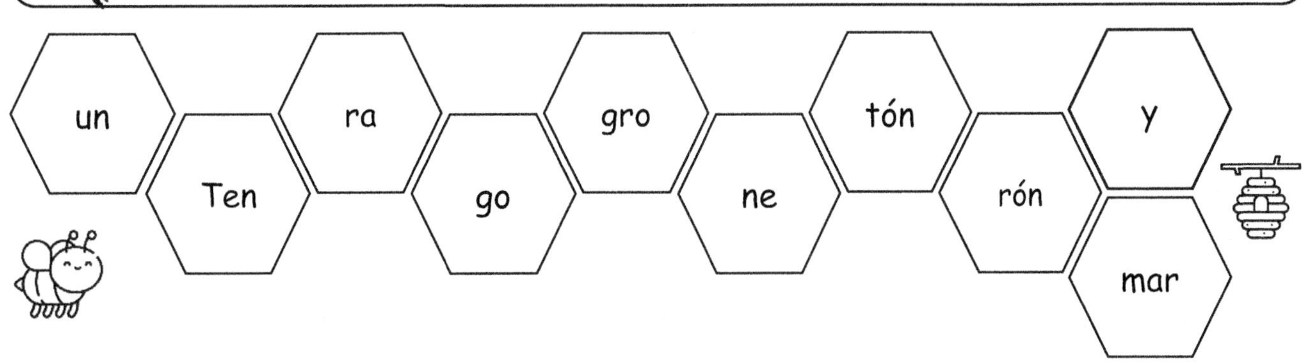

c. *I have a brown and black mouse:* T__________ u___ r________ m____________ y n__________.

2. Read, Match, Find and Colour

A. Match these sentences to the pictures above

a. Tengo un conejo gris y rosa.
b. Tienes una tortuga verde y roja.
c. Tengo un pingüino blanco y negro.
d. No tengo una gallina amarilla.
e. Tengo un pez azul y amarillo.
f. Tengo un perro marrón y gris.
g. Tienes un gato pequeño.
h. No tienes una oveja blanca y rosa.
i. Tengo un loro naranja, rojo y azul.
j. Tengo un caballo grande.

B. Using the sentences in task A find the Spanish for:

a. A yellow chicken.
b. I have a fish.
c. A white sheep.
d. A green turtle.
e. Brown and grey.
f. A small cat.
g. A big horse.
h. I have a penguin.
i. You do not have.
j. I do not have.

3. True or False

Read the paragraphs below and then answer True or False

Hola, me llamo **Enrique** y tengo diez años. Mi cumpleaños es el cinco de junio. Tengo un caballo gris que se llama Zagor.

2. Hola, me llamo **Carlota** y tengo ocho años. Mi cumpleaños es el trece de mayo. Tengo un gato blanco que se llama Mate.

		True	False
1	a. **Enrique** is 10 years old.	✓	
	b. His birthday is on the 4th July.		✓
	c. He has a grey dog.		✓
	d. His pet is called Zagor.	✓	
2	a. **Carlota** is 7 years old.		✓
	b. Her birthday is on the 3rd March.		✓
	c. She has a white cat.	✓	
	d. Her cat is called Lola.		✓

4. Tick or Cross

A. Read the text. Tick the box if you find the words in the text, cross it if you do not find them.

- Hola, me llamo **Stefano.**

Tengo once años. Mi cumpleaños es el diecinueve de enero. Tengo un gato rojo y blanco que se llama Rómulo. Es un gato grande. ¿Tú tienes mascotas?

- Hola, me llamo **Belén.**

Tengo siete años. Mi cumpleaños es el doce de abril. Tengo un conejo negro y blanco que se llama Coco. Es un conejo pequeño.

	✓	✗
a. Me llamo	✓	
b. Trece años		✗
c. Un gato grande	✓	
d. Un conejo		✗
e. Un perro gris		✗
f. Que se llama		✗

g. I am 7 years old	✓	
h. My birthday	✓	
i. Black and brown		✗
j. Black and white	✓	
k. I have a cat		✗
l. Small rabbit	✓	

B. Find the Spanish in the texts above

a. My name is Me llamo ✓

b. My birthday is Mi cumpleanos es el ✓

c. It is a big cat. Es un gato grande. ✓

d. Do you have pets? ¿Tú tienes mascotas? ✓

e. I have a black rabbit. Tengo un conejo negro ✓

5. Language Detective

- Me llamo **José.** Tengo doce años. Mi cumpleaños es el quince de febrero. Tengo un pájaro amarillo que se llama Pajito, pero no tengo un perro negro.

- Me llamo **Carmen.** Tengo trece años. Mi cumpleaños es el veinte de enero. Tengo un ratón gris que se llama Zar, pero no tengo un pez azul.

- Hola, me llamo **Manuel.** Tengo seis años. Mi cumpleaños es el dos de junio. Tengo un loro verde que se llama Coco, pero no tengo un caballo blanco.

- Buenos días, me llamo **Nieves.** Tengo once años. Mi cumpleaños es el catorce de mayo. Tengo una cobaya marrón y blanca que se llama Coby.

A. Find someone who...

a. ...is 12 years old José ✓

b. ...has a green parrot Manuel ✓

c. ...has a grey mouse Carmen ✓

d. ...was born on the 2nd June Manuel ✓

e. ...does not have a black dog José ✓

f. ...was born in January Carmen ✓

g. ...has a guinea pig Nieves ✓

h. ...is 11 years old Nieves ✓

B. Put a cross in the box and underline the corresponding Spanish translation. One is odd.

My name is	a yellow bird	brown and white
I have a guinea pig	My birthday	I am 8 years old
which is called	I don't have	15th of February
a black dog	14th of May	but I don't have

Unit 5. I can say what pets I have: WRITING

1. Spelling

a. Tengo	*I have*
b. Un gato	*A cat*
c. vn caballo	*A horse*
d. Un perro marrón	*A brown dog*
e. Un loro amarillo	*A yellow parrot*
f. Tienes	*You have*
g. Una mascota	*A pet*

2. Anagrams

a. ogneT un roper ogren. — *I have a black dog.*

Tengo un perro negro

b. oN etong nu otag derve. — *I do not have a green cat.*

no tengo un gato verde

c. Mi vejao es allam Pape. — *My sheep is called Pepa.*

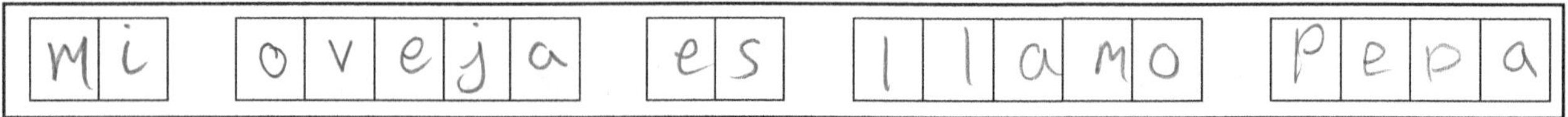

d. engoT anu troutag luza. — *I have a blue turtle.*

Tengo una tortuga azul

e. gnoTe anu yabaco ganer. — *I have a black guinea pig.*

Tengo una cobaya negra

3. Gapped Translation

a. Tengo siete años. — *I am* seven *years old.*

b. Tengo un gato pequeño. — *I have a* small *cat.*

c. No tengo araña. — *I do not have a* spider.

d. Tú tienes un caballo marrón. — I *have a brown* horse.

e. Tengo una oveja que se llama Dida. — *I have a sheep* called *Dida.*

f. Tengo un caballo blanco. — *I* have *a white* horse.

g. ¿Tienes mascotas? — *Do* you have *pets?*

h. No tengo mascotas. — *I do not have* pets.

i. Tengo una cobaya negra. — *I have a black* guinea pig.

4. Split Sentences

a. Tengo un	1. blanca
b. Una tortuga	2. gato
c. Tengo	3. un loro
d. Tengo una	4. negro
e. Un caballo	5. tengo mascotas
f. No	6. una mascota?
g. ¿Tienes	7. gallina

a	b	c	d	e	f	g
2	4	3	7	1	5	6

5. Rock Climbing

Starting from the bottom, pick one chunk from each row to translate the sentences in the grid below.

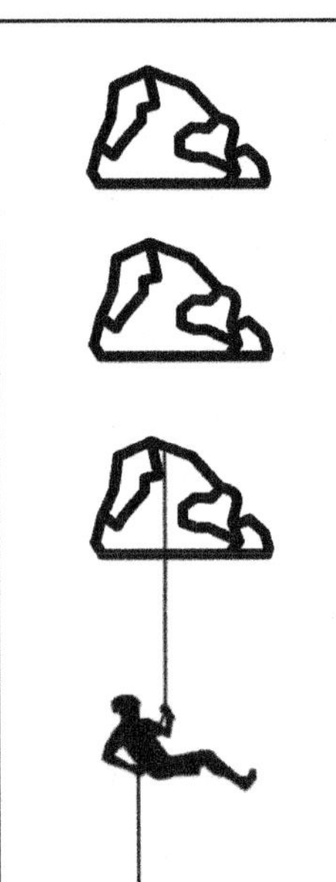

y rosa.	negro.	Rocky.	blanca.	y marrón.
pequeña	gallina	grande	llama	gato
un	se	una	una tortuga	un caballo
Mi perro	Tengo	No tengo	Tienes	No tienes
a.	b.	c.	d.	e.

a.	*My dog is called Rocky.*
Mi perro se llama Rocky	
b.	*I have a white chicken.*
Tengo una gallina blanca	
c.	*I don't have a black cat.*
No tengo un gato negro.	
d.	*You have a big and brown horse.*
Tienes un caballo grande y marrón.	
e.	*You do not have a small and pink turtle.*
No tienes una tortuga pequeña y rosa.	

6. Mosaic Translation

Use the words in the grid to help you translate the sentences below.

a.	Tengo	gato	Lucera	tengo	Dida.
b.	No tengo	tortuga	negro	y	un loro.
c.	Mi oveja	un pingüino	pequeña	y es	marrón.
d.	Mi perro	se llama	grande	negro y	blanco.
e.	Tengo una	es	pero	que se llama	blanca.

a. *I have a black and white penguin.*

Tengo un pingüino negro y blanco.

b. *I don't have a cat but I have a parrot.*

c. *My sheep is called Lucera and it is white.*

d. *My dog is big, black and brown.*

e. *I have a small tortoise which is called Dida.*

7. Sentence Puzzle

Put the words in the correct order

a. Tengo perro un marrón. ______________________

b. ¿una Tienes mascota? ______________________

c. un loro Tienes. ______________________

d. Tengo gato blanco un. ______________________

e. gallina Tengo una pequeña. ______________________

f. un azul pez Tienes amarillo y. ______________________

g. Tengo blanca cobaya una. ______________________

h. tengo mascotas No. ______________________

i. gato Tengo y blanco negro un. ______________________

8. Tangled Translation

a. Write the Spanish words in English to complete the translation

Hello, **me llamo** Dylan. I am **siete años**. **Mi cumpleaños** is on the **dieciocho de** July. **Tengo un** white dog **que se llama** Lily. **Es muy** big.

b. Write the English words in Spanish to complete the translation

Hello, me llamo Gianfranco. **I am** nueve **years old**. Mi **birthday** es el veinte **of June**. **I have a blue fish** que se llama Nemo. Es muy **small**.

9. Fill in the Gaps

a. Hola, me __________ Enrique y tengo diez años. Mi cumpleaños es el

_______ de junio. ________ un caballo _______ que se ______ Zar.

llamo	tengo	cinco	gris	llama

b. Hola, me llamo Carlos. Tengo _________ años. Mi cumpleaños es el

diecinueve de ________. Tengo un ________ marrón y _______ que

se llama Coby . Es ______________.

pequeño	perro	blanco	enero	once

10. Guided Translation

a. M__ ll_______ S____________ y t_______ o_______ a_______.

My name is Stefano and I am 11 years old.

b. T______ u__ c__________ g______ q___ s__ ll______ P_____.

I have a grey rabbit, which is called Pepe.

c. N__ t_______ u__ l_______, p_______ t________ u__ g_________.

I do not have a parrot, but I have a chicken.

d. T_______ u___, p_______ m_________ y u___ g______ n_______.

You have a brown dog and a black cat.

e. N__ t_______ u___ t___________, p___ t_______ u___ a_______.

You do not have a tortoise, but you have a spider.

f. N___ t_________ u___ c________________ b______________.

I do not have a white guinea pig

11. Pyramid Translation

Starting from the top, translate chunks into Spanish. Write the sentences in the box below.

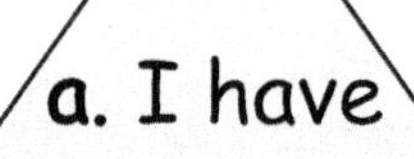

b. I have a white bird

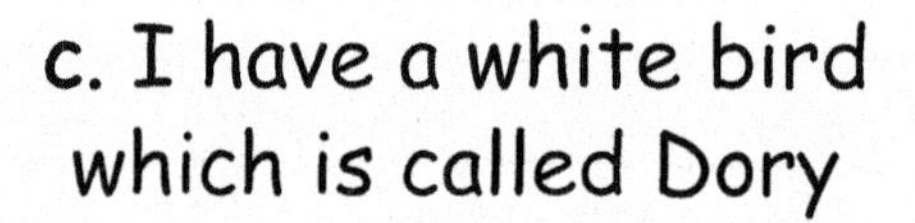

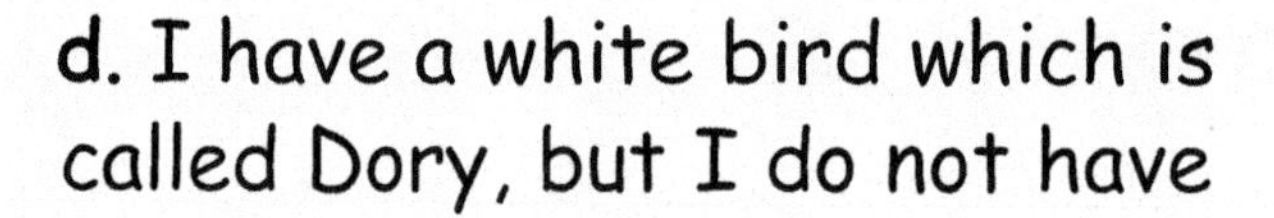

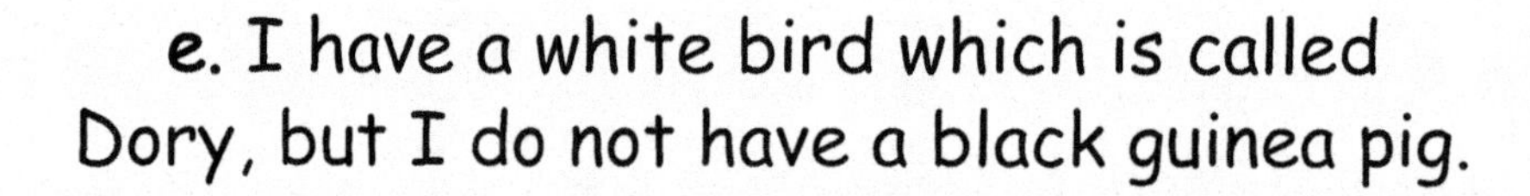

a.
b.
c.
d.
e.

12. Staircase Translation

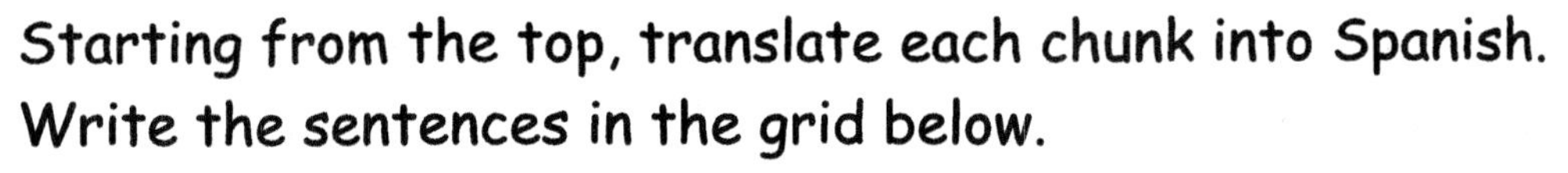

Starting from the top, translate each chunk into Spanish.
Write the sentences in the grid below.

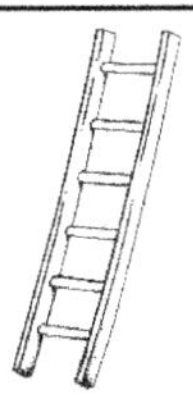

a.	Do you have	a dog?				
b.	I do not have	a white	sheep.			
c.	You have	a black	horse	which is called Zar.		
d.	I have	a brown	cat	and	a big tortoise.	
e.	I have	a small fish	and	you have	a grey	penguin.

Answers / Respuestas	
a.	
b.	
c.	
d.	
e.	

Challenge / Desafío

Can you create 2 more sentences using the words in the staircase grid?

☆	
☆	

UNIT 5 - MI MASCOTA

LISTENING

1. Listen and complete with the missing vowel

a. Un perro
b. Un caballo
c. Un gato
d. Un pez
e. Una tortuga
f. Una oveja
g. Un conejo
h. Una gallina

2. Listen and tick the word you hear

a. 2 b. 3 c. 1 d. 2 e. 3

3. Complete with the missing syllables in the box below

a. Un perro ne**gro**
b. Una **ga**llina blanca
c. Un ca**ba**llo gris
d. Un pez a**zul**
e. Un cone**jo** marrón
f. Una a**ra**ña negra
g. Una oveja ro**ja**
h. Un loro amari**llo**

4. Complete the words with the missing endings

a. Un pájaro amarillo
b. Una oveja rosa
c. Un loro rojo
d. Un gato negro
e. Una tortuga naranja
f. Un perro blanco
g. Un pingüino pequeño
h. Una gallina negra
i. Un pez verde
j. Una cobaya blanca

5. Write the missing word as you hear it - Students trsnscribe as they hear it

a. Un **pájaro** azul
b. Una **araña** amarilla
c. Un **conejo** rosa
d. Un **pingüino** negro
e. Una **cobaya** blanca
f. Una **oveja** roja
g. Un perro **marrón**
h. Un ratón **pequeño**
i. Una **gallina** grande
j. Tengo un **loro.**
k. **No** tengo un gato.

6. Faulty echo

a. No tengo un **pingüino** gris.
b. Tengo una **oveja** rosa.
c. No **tienes** un pez azul.
d. No tengo un gato **pequeño.**
e. Tienes una **gallina** pequeña.
f. No tienes un **caballo** marrón.
g. No tengo **mascotas.**
h. Tengo una tortuga **verde.**
i. Tengo un **loro** amarillo.
j. No tengo una araña **roja.**

7. Listen and choose the correct spelling

a. 2 b. 1 c. 2 d. 2 e. 2 f. 1 g. 1 h. 2 i. 1 j. 2 k. 1 l. 2

8. Fill in the grid - in English

a. Cat ; Black
b. Bird ; Blue
c. Sheep ; White
d. Parrot ; Yellow
e. Fish ; Orange
f. Rabbit ; White

9. Spot the intruder

Identify the word in each sentence the speaker is NOT saying

a. Tengo un pez azul y un <u>dos</u> gato gris.	**dos**
b. ¿Tienes <u>un</u> mascotas? No, no tengo mascotas.	**un**
c. Tú tienes un caballo blanco que <u>como</u> se llama Rocky.	**como**
d. Yo tengo un perro marrón y <u>no</u> grande.	**no**
e. Tú no tienes una araña <u>grande</u> pero tienes un ratón pequeño.	**grande**
f. Yo tengo un pingüino gris <u>blanco</u> que se llama Pepe.	**blanco**

10. Catch it, Swap it

Listen, spot the difference between what you hear and the written text and edit each sentence accordingly.

Transcript

e.g. Tengo un **conejo** *marrón y blanco.*	***<u>conejo</u>***
a. Tienes un caballo **pequeño** y gris.	**<u>pequeño</u>**
b. No tengo una **oveja** negra y amarilla.	**<u>oveja</u>**
c. Tengo un **perro,** pero no tengo una oveja.	**<u>perr</u>**
d. No tienes un pez **verde** pero tienes una araña.	**<u>verde</u>**
e. ¿Tienes una mascota? Sí, tengo un **caballo** negro.	**<u>caballo</u>**
f. No tengo un **ratón** pero tengo una cobaya.	**<u>ratón</u>**
g. Tengo un loro **amarillo** que se llama Rocky.	**<u>amarillo</u>**

11. Listening Slalom

e.g. Yo tengo un gato negro.	*(I have a black cat.)*
a. Tú tienes un caballo rosa.	(You have a pink horse.)
b. Yo no tengo un conejo amarillo.	(I don't have a yellow rabbit.)
c. Yo tengo un perro gris.	(I have a grey dog.)
d. Tú no tienes un ratón marrón.	(You don't have a brown mouse.)
e. Tengo una tortuga azul.	(I have a blue tortoise.)
f. Yo no tengo un pez blanco.	(I don't have a white fish.)

READING

1. Sylla-Bees

a. **Tengo un perro blanco.** b. **Tienes un loro azul y rosa.** c. **Tengo un ratón marrón y negro.**

2. Read, Match, Find and Colour

A. Match these sentences to the pictures above

a. Rabbit b. Turtle c. Penguin d. Chicken e. Fish f. Dog g. Cat
h. Sheep i. Parrot j. Horse

B. Using the sentences in task A find the Spanish for:

A. Una gallina amarilla. b. Tengo un pez. c. Una oveja blanca. d. Una tortuga verde.
E. Marrón y gris. f. Un gato pequeño. g. Un caballo grande. h. Tengo un pingüino.
I. No tienes. j. No tengo.

3. True or False

1 a. True b. False (5th of June) c. False (a grey horse) d. True

2 a. False (8) b. False (13th of May) c. True d. False (Mate)

4. Tick or Cross

A. Read the text. Tick the box if you find the words in the text, cross it if you do not find them

a. ✓ b. X c. ✓ d. X e. X f. ✓ g. ✓ h. ✓ i. X j. ✓ k. X l. ✓

B. Find the Spanish in the text above

a. Me llamo... b. Mi cumpleaños es el... c. Es un gato grande.
d. ¿Tú tienes mascotas? e. Tengo un conejo negro.

5. Language Detective

A. Find someone who...

a. José b. Manuel c. Carmen d. Manuel e. José f. Carmen g. Nieves h. Nieves

B. Odd one out: I am 8 years old. (odd chunk)

WRITING

1. Spelling

a. T**e**ngo b. U**n** ga**to** c. U**n** cab**a**llo d. Un p**e**rr**o** m**a**rr**ó**n e. Un l**o**ro **a**marillo
f. T**i**enes g. **M**ascotas

2. Anagrams

a. Tengo un perro negro. b. No tengo un gato verde. c. Mi oveja se llama Pepa.
d. Tengo una tortuga azul. e. Tengo una cobaya negra.

3. Gapped Translation

a. I am **seven** years old. b. I have a **small** cat. c. I do not have a **spider.**
d. **You** have a brown **horse.** e. I have a sheep **called** Dida. f. I **have** a white **horse.**
g. Do **you have** pets? h. I do not have **pets.** i. I have a black **guinea pig.**

4. Split Sentences

a. 2 b. 1 c. 3 d.7 e. 4 f.5 g.6

5. Rock Climbing

a. Mi perro se llama Rocky. b. Tengo una gallina blanca. c. No tengo un gato negro.
d. Tienes un caballo grande y marrón. e. No tienes una tortuga pequeña y rosa.

6. Mosaic Translation

a. Tengo un pingüino negro y blanco. b. No tengo un gato, pero tengo un loro.
c. Mi oveja se llama Lucera y es blanca. d. Mi perro es grande, negro y marrón.
e. Tengo una tortuga pequeña que se llama Dida.

7. Sentence Puzzle

a. Tengo un perro marrón. b. ¿Tienes una mascota? c. Tienes un loro.
d. Tengo un gato blanco. e. Tengo una gallina pequeña f. Tienes un pez azul y amarillo.
g. Tengo una cobaya blanca. h. No tengo mascotas. i. Tengo un gato blanco y negro.

8. Tangled Translation

a. Hello, **my name is** Dylan. I am **seven years old. My birthday** is on the **18th of** July. **I have a** white dog **which is called** Lily. **She is very** big.

b. **Hola,** me llamo Gianfranco. **Tengo** nueve **años**. Mi **cumpleaños** es el veinte **de junio**. **Tengo un pez azul** que se llama Nemo. Es muy **pequeño.**

9. Fill in the Gaps

a. Hola, me **llamo** Enrique y tengo diez años. Mi cumpleaños es el **cinco** de junio. **Tengo** un caballo **gris** que se **llama** Zar.

b. Hola, me llamo Carlos. Tengo **once** años. Mi cumpleaños es el diecinueve de **enero**. Tengo un **perro** marrón y **blanco** que se llama Maya. Es **pequeño**.

10. Guided Translation

a. **Me** llamo **Stefano** y **tengo** once **años.**

b. **Tengo un** conejo **gris** que se llama **Pepe.**

c. No **tengo loro, pero tengo un** gato.

d. **Tienes un perro marrón** y **un** gato **negro.**

e. No **tienes una tortuga, pero tienes una araña.**

f. No **tengo una cobaya** blanca.

11. Pyramid Translation

Tengo un pájaro blanco que se llama Dory, pero no tengo una cobaya negra.

12. Staircase Translation

a. ¿Tienes un perro?

b. No tengo una oveja blanca.

c. (Tú) Tienes un caballo negro que se llama Zar.

d. Tengo un gato marrón y una tortuga grande.

e. Tengo un pez pequeño y tú tienes un pingüino gris.

UNIT 6

MI MOCHILA

In this unit you will learn how to say in Spanish:

- ✓ What items you have in your pencil case/school bag
- ✓ What colour are your school items

You will revisit:

- ★ How to use *tengo/tienes*
- ★ *Hay/no hay*
- ★ Indefinite articles *un/una*
- ★ Word order noun + adjective

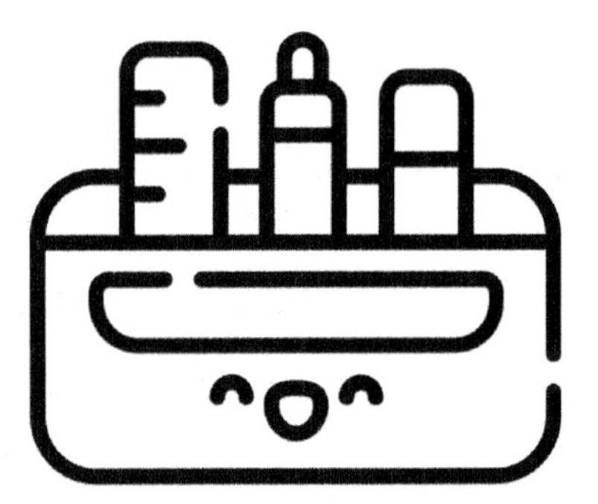

Tengo un estuche blanco

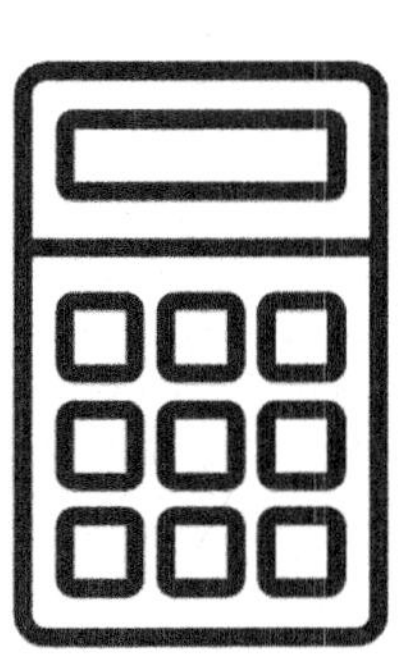

Tengo una calculadora roja

UNIT 6. MI MOCHILA
I can say what's in my schoolbag

¿Qué tienes en tu mochila? *What do you have in your schoolbag?*
¿Qué hay en tu estuche? *What's in your pencil case?*

<table>
<tr>
<td rowspan="2">En mi mochila
In my schoolbag

En mi estuche
In my pencil case</td>
<td rowspan="2">tengo
I have

hay
there is

no tengo
I have not

no hay
there is not</td>
<td>un
a</td>
<td>bolígrafo pen
cuaderno exercise book
estuche pencil case
lápiz pencil
lápiz de color
coloured pencil
libro book
pegamento glue
sacapuntas
pencil sharpener
rotuladres (couleringpens)</td>
<td>amarillo yellow
blanco white
negro black
rojo red

azul blue
gris grey
marrón brown
naranja orange
rosa pink
verde green</td>
</tr>
<tr>
<td>una
a</td>
<td>agenda planner
calculadora calculator
carpeta folder
goma rubber
regla ruler</td>
<td>amarilla yellow
blanca white
negra black
roja red

azul blue
gris grey
marrón brown
naranja orange
rosa pink
verde green</td>
</tr>
</table>

Unit 6. I can say what's in my schoolbag: LISTENING

1. Faulty Echo

e.g. En mi tengo un libro.

a. En mi estuche hay un pegamento.

b. ¿Qué tienes en tu mochila?

c. En mi mochila tengo una calculadora.

d. En mi estuche tengo una regla.

e. En mi mochila hay un cuaderno.

f. En mi estuche tengo una goma y un bolígrafo.

2. Listen and Match

a.	1.	
b.	2.	
c.	3.	
d.	4.	
e.	5.	
f.	6.	

3. Listen and tick the word you hear

	1	2	3
e.g.	*Carpeta* ✓	*Calculadora*	*Cuaderno*
a.	Mochila	Bolígrafo	Lápiz
b.	Agenda	Estuche	Libro
c.	Lápiz	Sacapuntas	Lápiz de color
d.	Tengo	Goma	Hay
e.	Pegamento	Hay	No hay

4. Fill in the grid with the correct information in English 

		Item	Colour
e.g.	*José*	*Calculator*	*Red*
a.	Pilar		
b.	Mario		
c.	Dylan		
d.	Valle		

5. Listen and complete with the missing vowels

a. Una calc__lador__.

b. Un l__bro az__l.

c. Un s__cap__ntas.

d. Una carp__ta.

e. Una moch__la.

f. Un bolígr__fo negr__.

g. Una carp__ta roj__.

h. Un p__gamento amarill__.

i. Un__ mochila v__rde.

j. Un láp__z de color r__sa.

a
e
i
o
u

6. Complete with the missing syllables in the box below

a. Un _ _ gamento amarillo.

b. Un _ _ piz de color verde.

c. Una a _ _ _ da roja.

d. Un bo _ _ grafo negro.

e. Un e _ _ _ che amarillo.

f. Una mo _ _ _ la blanca.

g. Tengo un sacapuntas ro_ _.

h. Una cal _ _ ladora negra.

i. ¿Qué _ _ _ nes en tu estuche?

j. Una car _ _ ta naranja.

gen	stu	jo	pe	lá	pe	lí	cu	chi	tie

7. Can you help the penguin to break the flow?

Draw a line between words

8. Spot the Intruder

Identify the words in each sentence the speaker is NOT saying

a. En mi estuche no hay un bolígrafo azul.

b. En mi estuche tengo hay una goma y un pegamento.

c. En mi estuche hay una goma, un sacapuntas y una regla.

d. ¿Qué tienes en tu un estuche?

e. ¿Qué tengo hay en tu mochila?

f. En mi mochila no tengo una agenda amarilla y verde.

g. En mi mochila hay un lápiz, un libro y un cuaderno rojo.

9. Catch it, Swap it

Listen, spot the difference between what you hear and the written text and edit each sentence accordingly.

e.g. En mi mochila tengo una goma.	*estuche*
a. En mi mochila tengo un pegamento verde.	
b. En mi estuche hay un bolígrafo negro.	
c. En mi mochila hay una calculadora rosa.	
d. En mi mochila no tengo una agenda azul.	
e. En mi estuche no hay un lápiz amarillo.	
f. En mi mochila no hay una agenda roja.	
g. No tengo un cuaderno rojo.	

10. Sentence bingo

Write 4 of the sentences into the grid. You will hear sentences in Spanish in a RANDOM ORDER. Tick all 4 of your sentences to win bingo.

1. En mi mochila hay una calculadora rosa.
2. En mi mochila tengo un pegamento verde.
3. En mi mochila no tengo una agenda azul.
4. En mi mochila tengo un pegamento.
5. No tengo un cuaderno rojo.
6. En mi estuche no hay un lápiz amarillo.
7. En mi mochila no hay una agenda roja.
8. Tengo un boli.
9. No tengo un boli verde.
10. En mi estuche hay un bolígrafo negro.

	BINGO

11. Listening Slalom

Listen and pick the equivalent English words from each column

e.g. *Tengo un lápiz gris y una goma*

Listening Word Order Alert! ((!))

You will hear: *Tengo un lápiz* (a pencil) *gris* (grey), as colours and adjectives follow the noun in Spanish.

e.g.	***I have***	there is	calculator	but there is a ruler.
a.	In my pencil case	***a grey***	a sharpener	***and a rubber.***
b.	In my schoolbag	I have	***pencil***	and a red folder.
c.	I have a black pen	there isn't	a blue book	in my pencil case.
d.	I don't have	folder but I don't have	a yellow ruler	in my schoolbag.
e.	In my pencil case	and a	I have	and a pink pencil.
f.	I have an orange	a white rubber but	a red exercise book	a glue.

Challenge / Desafío

Can you read the sentences in Spanish? You could use a colour/pattern to identify the 3 chunks of each sentence!

Unit 6. I can say what's in my schoolbag: READING

1. Sylla-bees.
Read and put the syllables in the cells in the correct order

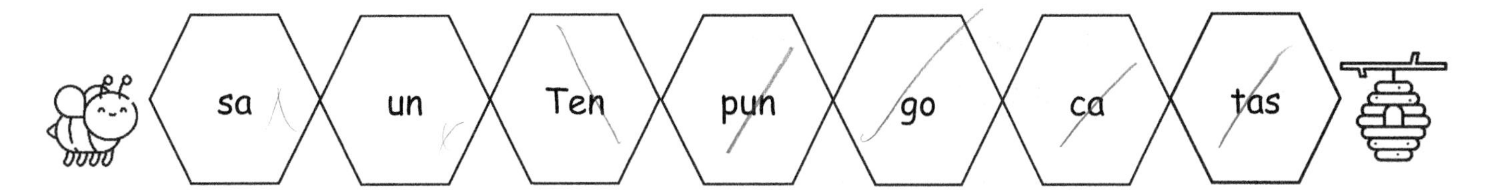

1. *I have a pencil sharpener.*
T*engo* u*n* s*acapuntas*.

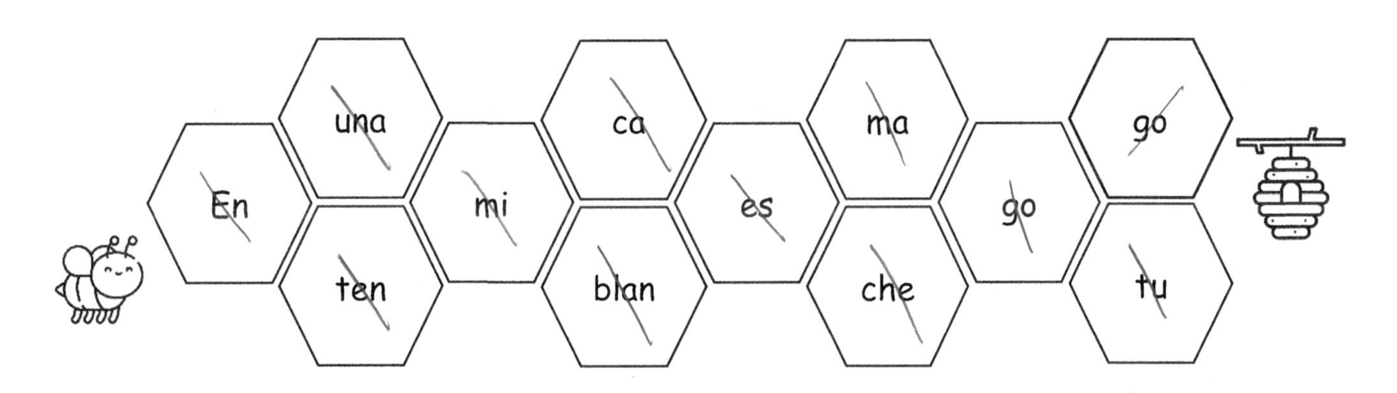

b. *In my pencil case I have a white rubber.*
E*n* m*i* e*stuche* t*engo* u*na* g*oma* b*lanca*.

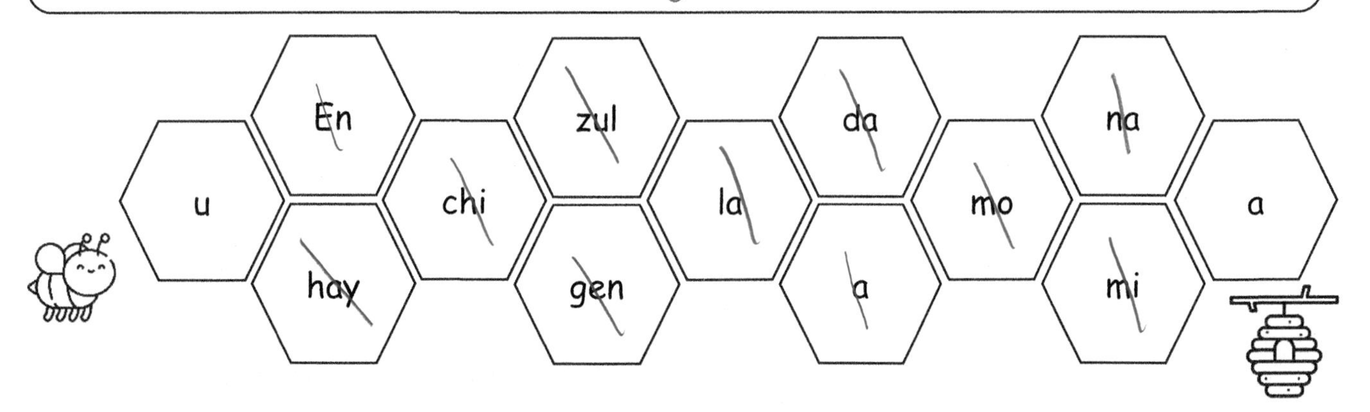

c. *In my schoolbag there is a blue planner.*
E*n* m*i* m*ochila* h*ay* u*na* a*agenda* a*zul*.

2. Read, Match, Find and Colour

A. Match these sentences to the pictures above

a. En mi estuche tengo un lápiz gris.
b. Tengo una mochila roja y negra.
c. En mi estuche hay una goma blanca.
d. ¿Tienes una calculadora?
e. Tengo un bolígrafo verde.
f. En mi mochila hay un libro amarillo.
g. Tengo un sacapuntas azul.
h. En mi estuche hay una regla rosa.
i. No tengo una agenda naranja.
j. En mi mochila tengo una carpeta.

B. Using the sentences in task A find the Spanish for:

a. A blue pencil sharpener.
b. I have a school bag.
c. In my pencil case.
d. There is a ruler.
e. A pink ruler.
f. I do not have.
g. I have a folder.
h. Red and black.
i. You have.
j. An orange diary.

3. True or False

A. Read the paragraphs below and then answer True or False

Hola, me llamo **Pedro** y tengo once años. Mi cumpleaños es el veintiuno de julio. Tengo un gato y una tortuga. En mi mochila hay un libro, una carpeta roja y un cuaderno amarillo, pero no hay una regla.

Hola, me llamo **Amira** y tengo nueve años. Mi cumpleaños es el treinta de noviembre. Tengo un conejo, pero no tengo un caballo. En mi estuche tengo un lápiz gris, un bolígrafo negro, una goma naranja, pero no tengo un sacapuntas.

	True	False
a. **Pedro** is 11 years old.	✓	
b. His birthday is on the 13th July.		✓
c. He has a dog and a cat.		✓
d. In his schoolbag there is a book.	✓	
e. He has a pink folder.	✓	
f. He does not have a ruler.	✓	
g. **Amira** is 10 years old.		✓
h. She has a dog but does not have a horse.		✓
i. In her pencil case she has a blue pen.		✓
j. She does not have a sharpener.	✓	

B. Find in the texts above the Spanish for:

a. My birthday is

b. In my schoolbag

c. I have a rabbit

d. A yellow workbook

e. I don't have a sharpener

f. An orange rubber

4. Tick or Cross

A. Read the texts. Tick the box if you find the words in the text, cross it if you do not find them.

a. Hola, me llamo **María**.

Tengo trece años. Mi cumpleaños es el quince de febrero. Tengo un pez que se llama Ricky. En mi mochila hay una calculadora, una carpeta amarilla y un pegamento, pero no hay una agenda rosa.

	✓	✗
a. Tengo trece años.	✓	
b. El doce de...		✗
c. En mi estuche.		✗
d. Una calculadora.	✓	
e. Un pegamento.	✓	
f. Pero no hay...		✗

b. Hola, me llamo **Juan**.

Tengo ocho años. Mi cumpleaños es el seis de julio. Tengo un conejo, pero no tengo una tortuga. En mi estuche tengo un sacapuntas, un lápiz y una regla blanca, pero no tengo una goma.

	✓	✗
g. I am 9 years old.		✗
h. The 7th of June.		✗
i. But I don't have...	✓	
j. In my pencil case.	✓	
k. A pencil.	✓	
l. And a ruler.	✓	

B. Find the Spanish in the texts above

a. The 15th of February. Es el quince de febrero

b. In my schoolbag. En mi mochila

c. A pink diary. una agenda

d. A white ruler. una regla blanca

e. I do not have a rubber. no tengo una goma

5. Language detective

- Me llamo **Ricardo**. Tengo diez años. Mi cumpleaños es el cinco de marzo. Tengo un caballo marrón. En mi mochila tengo una agenda roja y un libro, pero no tengo una carpeta blanca.

- Me llamo **Marta**. Tengo catorce años. Mi cumpleaños es el veinticuatro de mayo. Tengo un gato pequeño. En mi estuche tengo una calculadora y un cuaderno verde, pero no tengo un pegamento amarillo.

- Hola, soy **Enid**. Tengo once años. Mi cumpleaños es el treinta de abril. Tengo una tortuga grande. En mi mochila hay una regla amarilla y un bolígrafo negro, pero no hay un sacapuntas gris.

A. Find someone who...

a. ...is 14 years old Marta

b. ...has a red diary Ricardo

c. ...has a green exercise book Marta

d. ...has a yellow ruler Enid

e. ...does not have a white folder Ricardo

f. ...has a black pen Enid

g. ...is 10 years old Ricardo

B. Put a cross in the box and underline the corresponding Spanish translation. One is odd.

And a book	A big tortoise	The 30th of April
A green notebook	A white horse	I am 11 years old
A grey sharpener	But there is not	In my school bag
In my pencil case	A yellow glue	But I do not have

Unit 6. I can say what's in my schoolbag: WRITING

1. Spelling

a. Una regla — *A ruler*

b. Un libro — *A book*

c. Un lapiz — *A pencil*

d. Un sacapuntas — *A pencil sharpener*

e. Una agenda — *A diary*

f. una mochila — *A schoolbag*

g. un pegamento — *A glue*

2. Anagrams

a. eTngo uan rglae. — *I have a ruler.*

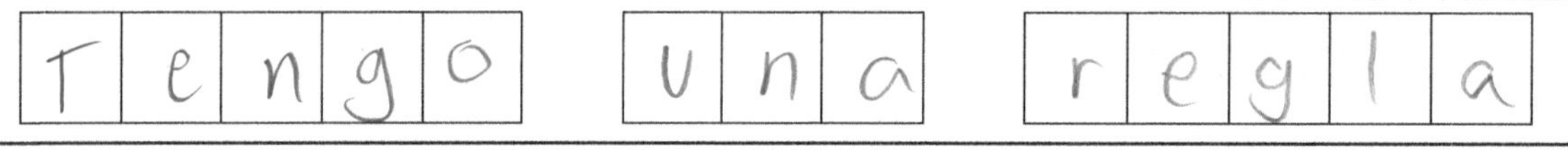

b. ieTnes aun omga. — *You have a rubber.*

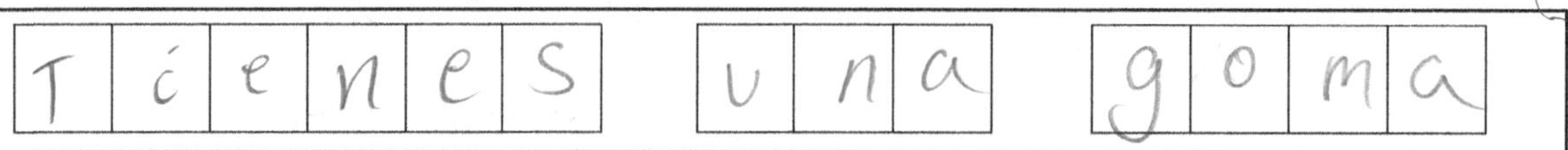

c. oN engot álzip. — *I don't have a pencil.*

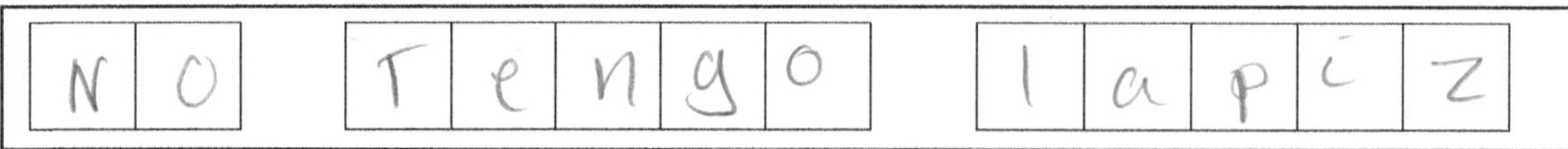

d. ensTie nu brilo. — *You have a book.*

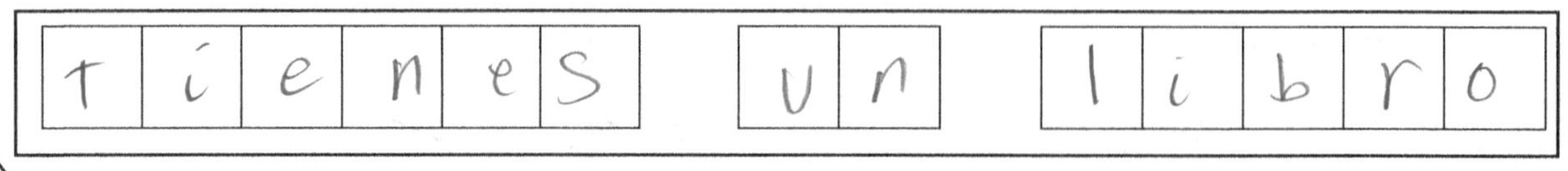

3. Gapped Translation

a. Tengo un lápiz naranja y un pegamento.

I have an ________ pencil and a ________ ________.

b. En mi estuche hay un bolígrafo verde y una regla.

In my pencil case there is a green ________ and a ________.

c. No tengo un sacapuntas, pero tengo una goma.

I do not have a ________, but I have a ________.

d. ¿Qué tienes en tu mochila? Tengo un libro.

________ do you ________ in your ________? I have a ________.

4. Split Sentences

a. Tengo un	1. tengo un lápiz.
b. En mi mochila	2. sacapuntas azul.
c. Tengo una	3. hay un libro.
d. No tengo	4. en tu estuche?
e. En mi estuche	5. un cuaderno verde.
f. ¿Qué tienes	6. negro.
g. No hay un bolígrafo	7. carpeta rosa.

5. Rock Climbing

Starting from the bottom, pick one chunk from each row to translate the sentences below.

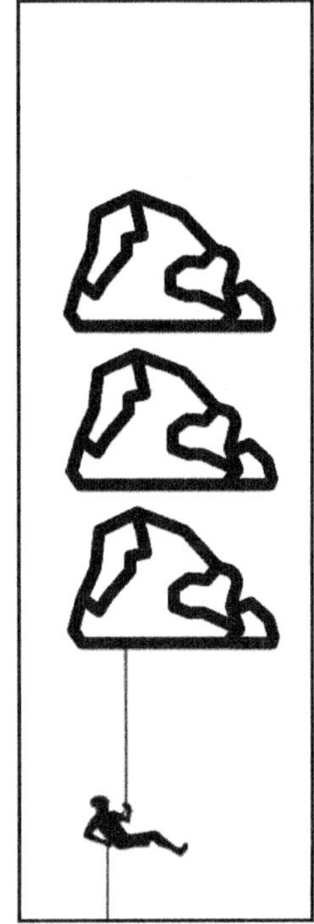

una agenda roja.	una carpeta.	una regla.	bolígrafo.	gris.
y un lápiz	un libro y	tengo un	pero tengo	pero no tengo
un pegamento	estuche	una goma amarilla	sacapuntas	hay
En mi	No tengo	Tienes	En mi mochila	Tengo un
a.	b.	c.	d.	e.

a. In my pencil case I have a pen.

en mi estuche tengo un bolígrago.

b. I do not have a glue stick, but I have a folder.

No tengo un pegamento pero tengo una carpeta.

c. You have a yellow rubber and a grey pencil.

Tienes una goma y un lápiz gríz.

d. In my schoolbag there is a book and a red diary.

en mi mochila hay un libro y una agenda roja.

e. I have a sharpener, but I do not have a ruler.

Tengo un sacapuntas pero no tengo una regla.

6. Mosaic Translation

Use the words in the grid to help you translate the sentences below.

a.	En mi	una calculadora	sacapuntas	Tengo un	goma rosa.
b.	Tengo un	mochila	negra	y un lápiz	estuche.
c.	En mi estuche	tienes	azul	y una	libro rojo.
d.	¿Qué	bolígrafo	en tu mochila?	en mi	naranja.
e.	No hay	tengo un	hay una	carpeta	verde.

a. *In my schoolbag there is an orange folder.*

En mi mochila hay una carpeta naranja.

b. *I have a blue pen and a green pencil.*

Tengo un bolígrafo azul y un lápiz verde.

c. *In my pencil case I have a pencil sharpener and a pink rubber.*

en mi estuche tengo un sacapuntas y una goma rosa

d. *What do you have in your schoolbag? I have a red book.*

¿Qué tienes en tu mochila? tengó un libro rojo

e. *There isn't a black calculator in my pencil case.*

No hay una calcudora negra en mi estuche.

7. Sentence Puzzle

Put the words in the correct order

a. mochila En libro tengo mi un verde

In my schoolbag I have a green book.

b. ¿en tu tienes Qué estuche?

What do you have in your pencil case?

c. En una regla hay amarilla mi estuche

In my pencil case there is a yellow ruler.

d. pero no un sacapuntas hay En estuche mi goma una hay

In my pencil case there is a sharpener, but there isn't a rubber.

8. Tangled Translation

a. Write the Spanish words in English to complete the translation

Hello, **me llamo** Jaume. **Tengo** nine years old. My birthday **es el veintiseis** of January. I have **un perro** brown **que se llama Miquel.** In my pencil case there is **una goma blanca y** a red ruler, but **no hay** a **sacapuntas** grey.

b. Write the English words in Spanish to complete the translation

Buenos días, **my name is** Ester. **I am** trece años. Mi cumpleaños **is on the 15th** de febrero. Tengo **a horse** negro que se llama Bandido. **In my schoolbag there is** un libro verde y **a yellow exercise book,** pero no hay **a pink folder.**

9. Fill in the gaps

a. Hola, me llamo Juan y ________ once años. Mi cumpleaños es el veinte ___ junio. En mi ___________ tengo un _________ , un bolígrafo y _______ goma _________.

una	lápiz	tengo	de	estuche	blanca

b. Hola, ____ llamo Carmen. Tengo un _______ gris. En mi mochila _____ un libro, un ______________ y un cuaderno _____________. Pero no hay _____________.

sacapuntas	hay	carpeta	me	amarillo	conejo

10. Guided Translation

a. E__ m__ m___________ h___ u___ a________ n_________.

In my schoolbag there is an orange diary.

b. E__ m__ e_________ t_______ u__ l_______ a_______.

In my pencil case I have a blue pencil.

c. N__ h____ u___ g_______ e__ m___ e______________.

There isn't a rubber in my pencil case.

d. N___ t_______ u___ r_______, p____ t_________ u__ l______.

I don't have a ruler, but I have a book.

e. T________ u___ e_________ r_______ e___ m__ m___________.

I have a red pencil case in my schoolbag.

11. Pyramid Translation

Starting from the top, translate each chunk in Spanish. Write the sentences in the box below.

a. In my

b. In my schoolbag I have...

c. In my schoolbag I have a yellow book.

d. In my schoolbag I have a yellow book and a red folder.

e. In my schoolbag I have a yellow book and a red folder, but I don't have a ruler.

a.
b.
c.
d.
e.

12. Staircase Translation

Starting from the top, translate each chunk into Spanish. Write the sentences in the grid below.

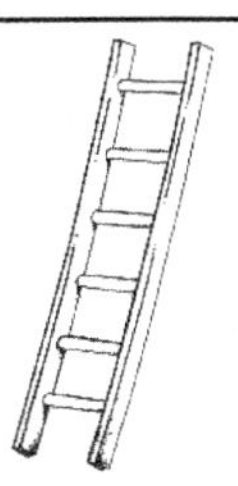

a.	I have a	red pen.				
b.	What	do you have	in your schoolbag?			
c.	In my pencil case	there is	a green pencil	and a ruler.		
d.	I don't have	a rubber	but	I have	a grey sharpener.	
e.	In my schoolbag	there isn't	a book	but there is	a calculator	and a diary.

Answers / Respuestas

a.	
b.	
c.	
d.	
e.	

Challenge / Desafío

Can you create 2 more sentences using the words in the staircase grid above?

☆	
☆	

Unit 5-6

No Snakes No Ladders

SALIDA	1 Tengo un gato	2 Tengo un caballo	3 Tengo una regla	4 En mi estuche	5 ¿Tienes una mascota?	6 No tengo mascotas	7 Una tortuga verde
15 Una cobaya marrón	14 Tengo un estuche verde	13 Un conejo grande	12 Un saca-puntas rojo	11 Un ratón gris	10 No tengo un pingüino	9 Hay una carpeta	8 Una oveja blanca
16 Tienes un loro	17 No tengo bolígrafo	18 Un perro negro	19 En mi mochila	20 Un pez azul	21 Tengo una goma	22 Tengo un lápiz	23 Que se llama Pepe
LLEGADA	30 Tienes una araña pequeña	29 Un pájaro amarillo	28 Tengo un cuaderno naranja	27 No tengo un bolígra-fo rosa	26 No hay una agenda blanca	25 No hay calculado-ra	24 Hay un libro azul

No Snakes No Ladders

SALIDA	1 I have a cat	2 I have a horse	3 I have a ruler	4 In my pencil case	5 Do you have a pet?	6 I don't have pets	7 A green tortoise
15 A brown guinea pig	14 I have a green pencil case	13 A big rabbit	12 A red pencil sharpener	11 A grey mouse	10 I don't have a penguin	9 There is a folder	8 A white sheep
16 You have a parrot	17 I don't have a pen	18 A black dog	19 In my school bag	20 A blue fish	21 I have a rubber	22 I have a pencil	23 Which is called Pepe
LLEGADA	30 You have A small spider	29 A yellow bird	28 I have an orange exercise book	27 I don't have a pink pen	26 There isn't a white planner	25 There isn't a calculator	24 There is a blue book

UNIT 6 - MI MOCHILA

LISTENING

1. Faulty Echo

*e.g. En mi **mochila** tengo un libro.* (mochayla)

a. En mi estuche **hay** un pegamento. (hey)

b. ¿**Qué** tienes en tu mochila? (kwe)

c. En mi mochila tengo una **calculadora**. (calcyuladora)

d. En mi estuche tengo una **regla**. (reglar/wriggler, English 'r')

e. **En** mi mochila hay un cuaderno. (in)

f. En mi estuche tengo una goma **y** un bolígrafo. (why)

2. Listen and Match

a. 2 b. 4 c. 6 d. 3 e. 1 f. 5

3. Listen and tick the word you hear

*e.g. En mi mochila tengo **una carpeta.***

a. 3 (lápiz) b. 1 (agenda) c. 2 (sacapuntas) d. 3 (hay) e. 1 (pegamento)

4. Fill in the grid with the correct information in English

e.g. Hola, me llamo José. En mi mochila hay una calculadora roja.

a. Buenos días me llamo Pilar. Tengo un bolígrafo negro.

b. Hola, me llamo Mario. En mi estuche hay una regla blanca.

c. Buenas tardes, me llamo Dylan. En mi mochila tengo un lápiz rosa.

d. Hola, me llamo Valle. No tengo un bolígrafo verde.

Answers:

*e.g. **Calculator / Red***

a. **Pen / Black**

b. **Ruler / White**

c. **Pencil / Pink**

d. **Pen / Green**

5. Listen and complete with the missing vowels

a. Una calc**u**lador**a**

b. Un libro az**u**l

c. Un s**a**cap**u**ntas

d. Una carp**e**ta

e. Una moch**i**la

f. Un bolígr**a**fo negr**o**

g. Una carp**e**ta roj**a**

h. Un p**e**gamento amarill**o**

i. Un**a** mochila v**e**rde

j. Un láp**i**z de color r**o**sa

6. Complete with the missing syllables in the box below

a. Un **pe**gamento amarillo.

b. Un **lá**piz de color verde.

c. Una a**gen**da roja.

d. Un bolígrafo negro.

e. Un e**stu**che amarillo.

f. Una mo**chi**la blanca.

g. Tengo un sacapuntas ro**jo**.

h. Una cal**cu**ladora negra.

i. ¿Qué **tie**nes en tu estuche?

j. Una car**pe**ta naranja.

7. Can you help the penguin to break the flow? Draw a line between words

a. En mi estuche hay un pegamento gris.

b. En mi mochila hay un libro y una regla.

c. ¿Qué tienes en tu mochila? Tengo un lápiz.

d. En mi estuche no tengo una goma blanca.

e. En mi mochila no hay una agenda rosa.

f. En mi estuche tengo un sacapuntas azul.

8. Spot the Intruder. Identify the word in each sentence the speaker is NOT saying

a. En mi estuche no hay un bolígrafo azul. **no**
b. En mi estuche tengo hay una goma y un pegamento. **hay**
c. En mi estuche hay una goma, un sacapuntas y una regla. **una goma**
d. ¿Qué tienes en tu un estuche? **un**
e. ¿Qué tengo hay en tu mochila? **tengo**
f. En mi mochila no tengo una agenda amarilla y verde. **y verde**
g. En mi mochila hay un lápiz, un libro y un cuaderno rojo. **un lápiz**

9. Catch it, Swap it.
Listen, spot the difference between what you hear and the written text and edit each sentence accordingly
Transcript

e.g. En mi ***estuche*** *tengo una goma.* ***estuche***
a. En mi mochila tengo un pegamento **rojo.** **rojo**
b. En mi estuche hay un bolígrafo **azul**. **azul**
c. En mi mochila hay una **carpeta** rosa **carpeta**
d. En mi mochila no tengo una agenda **naranja** **naranja**
e. En mi estuche no hay un **cuaderno** amarillo **cuaderno**
f. En mi mochila no **tengo** una agenda roja. **tengo**
g. No tengo un **sacapuntas** rojo **sacapuntas**

10. Sentence Bingo
Write 4 of the sentences into the grid. You will hear sentences in Spanish in a RANDOM ORDER. Tick all 4 of your sentences to win!

1. In my school bag I have a glue. ***En mi mochila tengo un pegamento.***
2. In my school bag I have a green glue. ***En mi mochila tengo un pegamento verde.***
3. In my pencil case there is a black pen. ***En mi estuche hay un bolígrafo negro.***
4. In my school bag there is a pink calculator. ***En mi mochila hay una calculadora rosa.***
5. In my school bag I do not have a blue diary. ***En mi mochila no tengo una agenda azul.***
6. In my pencil case there is not a yellow pencil. ***En mi estuche no hay un lápiz amarillo.***
7. In my school bag there is not a red diary. ***En mi mochila no hay una agenda roja.***
8. I do not have a red exercise book. ***No tengo un cuaderno rojo.***
9. I do not have a green pen. ***No tengo un boli verde.***
10. I have a pen. ***Tengo un boli.***

11. Listening Slalom
Listen and pick the equivalent English words from each column

e.g. Tengo un lápiz gris y una goma.
a. En mi estuche tengo una regla amarilla y un lápiz rosa. *(In my pencil case I have a yellow ruler and a pink pencil)*
b. En mi mochila hay un libro azul y una carpeta roja. *(In my schoolbag there is a blue book and a red folder)*
c. Tengo un bolígrafo negro y una calculadora en mi estuche. *(I have a black pen and a calculator in my pencil case)*
d. No tengo una goma blanca, pero tengo un pegamento. *(I don't have a white rubber, but I have a glue)*
e. En mi estuche no hay un sacapuntas, pero hay una regla. *(In my pencil case there isn't a sharpener, but there is a ruler)*
f. Tengo una carpeta naranja, pero no tengo un cuaderno rojo en mi mochila. *(I have an orange folder, but I don't have a red notebook in my schoolbag)*

READING

1. Sylla-Bees

a. **Tengo un sacapuntas.** b. **En mi estuche tengo una goma blanca.** c. **En mi mochila hay una agenda azul.**

2. Read, Match, Find and Colour

A. Match these sentences to the pictures above

a. Pencil b. Schoolbag c. Rubber d. Calculator e. Pen f. Book g. Sharpener h. Ruler i. Diary j. Folder

B. Using the sentences in task A find the Spanish for:

a. Un sacapuntas azul b. Tengo una mochila c. En mi estuche d. Hay una regla e. Una regla rosa f. No tengo g. Tengo una carpeta h. Roja y negra (f) i. Tienes j. Una agenda naranja

3. True or False

A. Read the paragraphs and for each statement answer True of False

a. True b. False (21st of July) c. False (cat and turtle) d. True e. False (yellow exercise book) f. True g. False (9) h. False (has a rabbit) i. False (black pen) c. True

B. Find in the text above the Spanish for:

a. Mi cumpleaños es b. En mi mochila c. Tengo un conejo d. un cuaderno amarillo e. No tengo un sacapuntas f. una goma naranja

4. Tick or Cross

A. Read the text. Tick the box if you find the words in the text, cross it if you do not find them

a. ✓ b. X c. X d. ✓ e. ✓ f. ✓ g. X h. X i. ✓ j. ✓ k. ✓ l. ✓

B. Find the Spanish in the text above

a. El quince de febrero b. En mi mochila c. Una agenda rosa d. una regla blanca e. No tengo goma

5. Language Detective

A. Find someone who...

a. Marta b. Ricardo c. Marta d. Enid e. Ricardo f. Enid g. Ricardo

B. Odd one out: A white horse (odd chunk)

WRITING

1. Spelling

a. Una **regla** b. Un **libro** c. Un **lápiz** d. Un **sacapuntas** e. Una **agenda** f. Una **mochila** g. Un **pegamento**

2. Anagrams

a. Tengo una regla b. Tienes una goma c. No tengo lápiz d. Tienes un libro

3. Gapped Translation

a. I have an **orange** pencil and a **glue stick.** b. In my pencil case there is a green **pen** and a **ruler.**
c. I do not have a **sharpener** but I have a **rubber.** d. **What** do you **have** in your **schoolbag**? I have a **book.**

4. Split Sentences

a. 2 b. 3 c. 7 d. 5 e. 1 f. 4 g. 6

5. Rock Climbing

a. En mi estuche tengo un bolígrafo.
b. No tengo un pegamento, pero tengo una carpeta.
c. Tienes una goma amarilla y un lápiz gris.
d. En mi mochila hay un libro y una agenda roja.
e. Tengo un sacapuntas, pero no tengo una regla.

6. Mosaic Translation

a. En mi mochila hay una carpeta naranja.
b. Tengo un bolígrafo azul y un lápiz verde.
c. En mi estuche tengo un sacapuntas y una goma rosa.
d. ¿Qué tienes en tu mochila? Tengo un libro rojo.
e. No hay una calculadora negra en mi estuche.

7. Sentence Puzzle

a. En mi mochila tengo un libro verde.
b. ¿Qué tienes en tu estuche?
c. En mi estuche hay una regla amarilla.
d. En mi estuche hay un sacapuntas pero no hay una goma.

8. Tangled Translation

a. Hello, **my name is** Jaume. **I am** nine years old. My birthday **is the 26th** of January. I have **a** brown **dog which is called Miquel.** In my pencil case there is **a white rubber and** a red ruler but **there is not** a grey **sharpener**.
b. Buenos días, **me llamo** Ester. **Tengo** trece años. Mi cumpleaños **es el quince** de febrero. Tengo **un caballo** negro que se llama Bandido. **En mi mochila hay** un libro verde y **un cuaderno amarillo**, pero no hay **una carpeta rosa.**

9. Fill in the Gaps

a. Hola, me llamo Juan y **tengo** once años. Mi cumpleaños es el veinte **de** junio. En mi **estuche** tengo un **lápiz**, un bolígrafo y **una** goma **blanca**.
b. Hola, **me** llamo Carmen. Tengo un **conejo** gris. En mi mochila **hay** un libro, un **sacapuntas** y un cuaderno **amarillo**. Pero no hay **carpeta**.

10. Guided Translation

a. **En** mi **mochila hay una** agenda **naranja.**
b. **En** mi **estuche tengo** un **lápiz** a**zul.**
c. **No hay una goma** en mi **estuche.**
d. **No tengo una regla, pero tengo un libro.**
d. T**engo un** e**stuche** r**ojo en** mi **mochila.**

11. Pyramid Translation

En mi mochila tengo un libro amarillo y una carpeta roja, pero no tengo una regla.

12. Staircase Translation

a. Tengo un bolígrafo rojo.
b. ¿Qué tienes en tu mochila?
c. En mi estuche hay un lápiz verde y una regla.
d. No tengo una goma, pero tengo un sacapuntas gris.
e. En mi mochila no hay un libro, pero hay una calculadora y una agenda.

UNIT 7

¿DE DÓNDE ERES?

In this unit you will learn how to:

- ✓ Say where you are from
- ✓ Say what languages you speak
- ✓ Use *soy/ no soy, eres/ no eres*
- ✓ *Hablo/no hablo, hablas/no hablas*
- ✓ Use some connectives
- ✓ Ask and understand what the weather is like

You will revisit:

- ★ Saying your age and birthday
- ★ Talking about your pets

¿De dónde eres?

Soy de España

UNIT 7. ¿DE DÓNDE ERES?

I can say where I am from and what languages I speak

¿De dónde eres? *[Where are you from?]*
¿Qué idiomas hablas? *[What languages do you speak?]*

Soy de *I am from*	Alemania *Germany* América Australia Argentina China Escocia *Scotland* España *Spain* Francia *France* Inglaterra *England* Irlanda *Ireland* Italia *Italy* Portugal	y *and* pero *but* también *also*	hablo *I speak* no hablo *I don't speak*	un poco de *a little* muy bien *very well*	alemán *German* chino *Chinese* español *Spanish* francés *French* galés *Welsh* inglés *English* irlandés *Irish* italiano *Italian* portugués *Portuguese*

Unit 7. Where I am from & languages I speak: LISTENING

1. Split sentences. Listen and match.

a. Soy de	1. eres?
b. Hablo	2. de China
c. No soy	3. Inglaterra
d. No hablo	4. España
e. ¿De dónde	5. hablas?
f. Soy de	6. llamas?
g. ¿Qué idiomas	7. francés
h. ¿Cómo te	8. español

2. Faulty Echo.

e.g. Soy de Argentina.

a. Soy de China.

b. Soy de España.

c. Hablo alemán.

d. Soy de Inglaterra.

e. Hablo inglés y francés.

f. Hablo italiano, pero no hablo portugués.

g. Hablo muy bien chino.

3. Listen and tick the word you hear

	1	2	3
a.	Inglaterra	inglés	francés
b.	alemán	chino	hablo
c.	España	español	soy
d.	China	chino	no
e.	Italia	Soy de	italiano

4. Fill in the grid with the correct information in English

		Country	Language
a.	Ronan		
b.	Alberto		
c.	Pamela		
d.	Ronaldo		

5. Listen and complete with the missing letters

a. Soy d__ Espa__a.

b. S__y de Fran__ia.

c. Hablo mu__ bi__n inglés.

d. No __ablo españo__.

e. Tamb__én habl__ alemán.

f. ¿Habl__s chin__? No, hablo galés.

g. So__ de Ch__na y hablo francés.

h. Habl__ francés y __n poco de italiano.

i. Soy de Port_gal y hablo portugué__.

j. ¿Habla__ ital__ano? Sí, muy bien.

6. Complete with the missing syllables in the box below

a. _ _ blo chino.

b. No ha_ _ _ alemán.

c. Soy de _ _ glaterra.

d. Hablo portu _ _ _ _.

e. ¿Hablas in _ _ _ _?

f. Soy de Es _ _ cia y hablo inglés.

g. Soy de Fran _ _ _ y hablo francés.

h. Soy de Espa _ _ y hablo un poco de chino.

i. No hablo muy bien espa _ _ _.

j. Tam _ _ _ _ hablo portugués.

glés	ha	co	gués	In	ña	cia	blo	ñol	bién

7. Can you help the penguin to break the flow?

Draw a line between words

8. Spot the Intruder

Identify the word in each sentence the speaker is NOT saying

a. Hablo inglés, español, pero no soy de Inglaterra.

b. Soy de Australia y no hablo un poco de chino.

c. Hablo alemán, pero también soy italiano.

d. ¿Hablas español? Sí, también soy francés.

e. No hablo galés, y pero hablo irlandés.

f. Soy de Portugal. Hablo portugués italiano.

g. No hablo chino hablas muy bien.

9. Catch it, Swap it

Listen, spot the difference between what you hear and the written text and edit each sentence accordingly

a. Soy de Italia y hablo muy bien italiano y francés.

b. Soy de Inglaterra y hablo inglés, pero no hablo chino.

c. Soy de Australia y hablo inglés, pero no hablo español.

d. Soy de América y hablo un poco de irlandés.

e. Soy de Escocia y hablo un poco de alemán.

f. Soy de Irlanda, pero no hablo muy bien inglés.

10. Sentence bingo

Write 4 of the sentences into the grid. You will hear sentences in Spanish in a RANDOM ORDER. Tick all 4 of your sentences to win

1. No hablo galés muy bien.
2. No hablo alemán.
3. Soy de Irlanda.
4. Hablo francés, pero no hablo portugués.
5. Hablo inglés, pero no hablo español.
6. Hablo un poco de chino.
7. Soy de Inglaterra.
8. Hablo muy bien portugués.
9. Soy de Italia.
10. Soy de Australia y hablo muy bien italiano.

11. Listening Slalom

Listen in Spanish and pick the equivalent English words from each column.

e.g. Soy de China y hablo muy bien chino.

Colour in the boxes for each sentence in a different colour.

e.g.	***I am from***	I am from	but I do not speak	I speak Spanish.
a.	My name is Stefano	***China and***	Irish	Germany.
b.	Hello	England	***I speak very well***	*French.*
c.	I am	I speak Spanish	Italy but	***Chinese.***
d.	I speak	from Spain	but I am from	I speak Portuguese.
e.	You don't speak	a bit of Chinese	and I speak a a bit of	English.
f.	I am not from	very well	I am from Argentina and	but you speak Italian.

Unit 7. Where I am from & languages I speak: READING

1. Sylla-Bees

Read and put the syllables in the cells in the correct order

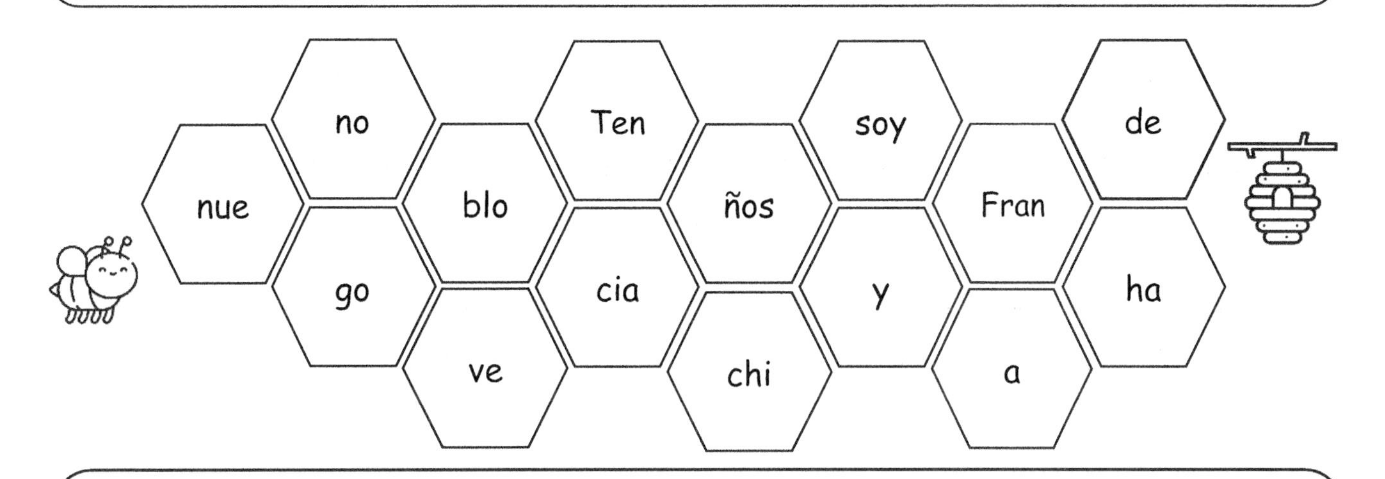

a. *I am nine years old, I am from France and I speak Chinese.*

T_____ n_____ a____, s___ d__ F_____ y h_____ c_____

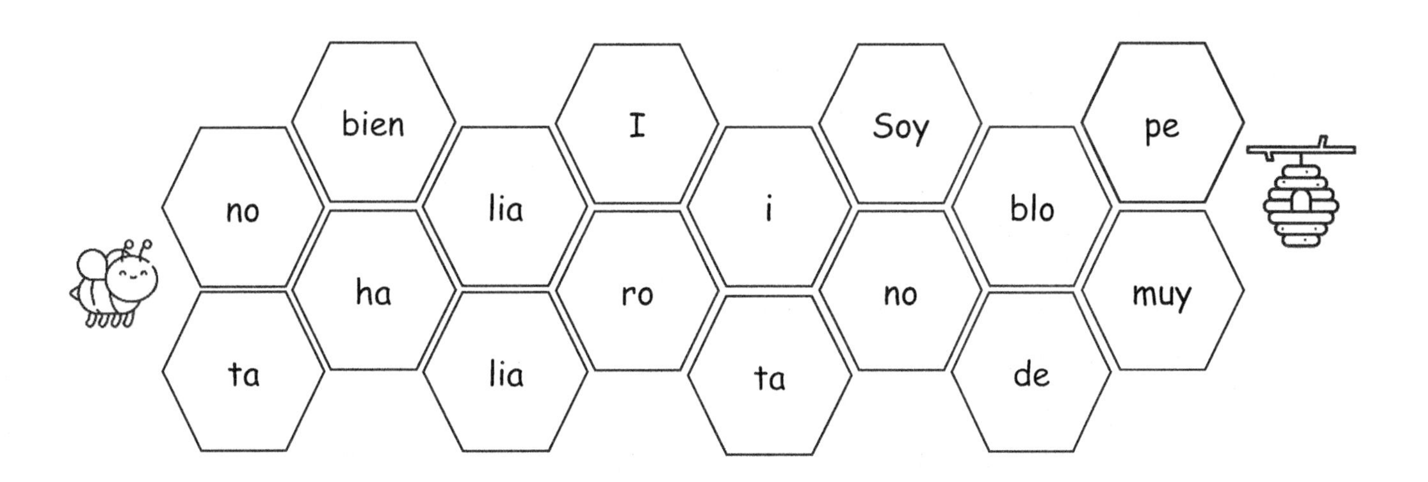

b. *I am from Italy, but I don't speak Italian very well.*

S___ d__ I_____, p____ n__ h_____ m___ b____ i______

2. True or False

A. Read the paragraphs below and then answer True or False

Hola, me llamo **Dylan**. Tengo trece años y tengo una perrita que se llama Lily. Tiene un año y es muy buena. Soy de España y hablo muy bien inglés y francés. También hablo un poco de portugués, pero no hablo alemán. Me gusta mucho el español.

Hola, me llamo **Simona**. Tengo doce años y no tengo mascotas. Soy de Italia y hablo muy bien italiano e inglés. También hablo un poco de francés, pero no hablo chino. Me gusta hablar el español, pero no me gusta nada el alemán.

	True	False
a. **Dylan** is 13 years old.		
b. He has a little cat.		
c. He speaks French very well.		
d. He speaks English and French.		
e. He doesn't speak German.		
f. He doesn't like Spanish.		
g. **Simona** is French.		
h. She speaks Italian and English a little.		
i. She doesn't speak Chinese.		
j. She doesn't like speaking in Spanish.		

B. Find in the texts above the Spanish for:

a. It is one year old.
b. It is very good.
c. I do not have pets.
d. I really like...
e. I like to speak...
f. I don't like it at all.

3. Tick or Cross

A. Read the texts. Tick the box if you find the words in the text, cross it if you do not find them.

- Hola, me llamo **Patricia.**

Tengo nueve años. Mi cumpleaños es el quince de octubre. Soy de Australia y hablo muy bien inglés e italiano. También hablo un poco de portugués, pero no hablo chino. Me gusta mucho el alemán.

	✓	✗
a. El quince de marzo.		
b. Soy de Francia.		
c. No hablo nada.		
d. Hablo español.		
e. No hablo chino.		
f. No me gusta.		

- Hola, me llamo **Pablo.**

Tengo ocho años. Soy de Escocia y hablo muy bien inglés y francés. También hablo un poco de irlandés, pero no hablo italiano. No me gusta nada el español.

g. I am 6 years old.		
h. I am from Spain.		
i. I speak English.		
j. I speak Italian.		
k. I don't speak.		
l. I don't like at all.		

B. Find the Spanish in the texts above

a. The 15th of October. ______________________

b. I do not speak Chinese. ______________________

c. I speak English very well. ______________________

d. I really like German. ______________________

e. I do not like Spanish at all. ______________________

4. Language Detective

- Me llamo **Ricardo**. Tengo cinco años. Mi cumpleaños es el nueve de noviembre. Soy de América y hablo muy bien francés y alemán. También hablo un poco de portugués, pero no hablo español. No me gusta el irlandés.

- Me llamo **Martina.** Tengo trece años. Mi cumpleaños es el doce de marzo. Tengo un caballo marrón que se llama Artex. Soy de Irlanda y hablo muy bien irlandés y español. También hablo un poco de chino. Me gusta el español.

- Hola, me llamo **Carmen.** Tengo once años. Mi cumpleaños es el veinte de junio. Soy de España y me gusta el inglés. Hablo muy bien español y alemán. También hablo un poco de chino, pero no hablo francés.

A. Find someone who...

a. ...is 13 years old.

b. ...has a brown horse.

c. ...likes English.

d. ...speaks Chinese a little (2).

e. ...speaks French very well.

f. ...speaks German very well (2).

g. ...doesn't speak French.

B. Put a cross in the box and underline the corresponding Spanish translation. One is odd.

I am five years old.	I like English.	But I don't speak French.
I speak Portuguese a little.	The 12th of March.	I speak Chinese a little.
I am from America.	I like Spanish.	I don't like Spanish.
I don't like Irish.	The 20th of June.	I am from Spain.

Unit 7. Where I am from & languages I speak: WRITING

1. Spelling

a. A ___ ___ ___ á ___ — *German*

b. U ___ ___ o ___ ___ — *A little*

c. A ___ ___ ___ a ___ ___ ___ — *Germany*

d. I ___ ___ ___ a ___ ___ ___ r ___ — *England*

e. I ___ ___ ___ é ___ — *English*

f. H ___ ___ ___ o e ___ ___ ___ ñ ___ ___ — *I speak Spanish.*

g. N ___ ___ ___ ___ l ___ c ___ ___ ___ ___ ___ — *I don't speak Chinese.*

2. Anagrams

a. blHoa lepsoañ. — *I speak Spanish.*

b. ySo ed glateInarr. — *I am from England.*

c. oN bloah manáel. — *I don't speak German.*

d. eM ugast le salgé. — *I like Welsh.*

e. Holba tuporgusé. — *I speak Portuguese.*

3. Gapped Translation

a. Hablo alemán y francés, pero no hablo inglés.

I speak ________ and _________, but I don't speak _______.

b. Soy de Alemania y hablo muy bien irlandés.

I am from _________ and I speak Irish ______ _______.

c. Soy de Inglaterra, pero no hablo inglés.

I am from ___________, but I don't speak __________.

d. ¿Qué idiomas hablas? Hablo irlandés.

What ___________ do you ________? I speak __________.

4. Split Sentences

a. Hablo muy

b. No hablo

c. Hablo un

d. Hablo un poco

e. No

f. ¿Qué idiomas

g. ¿De dónde

1. hablas?
2. portugués.
3. de inglés.
4. bien inglés.
5. poco de francés.
6. hablo chino.
7. eres?

a	b	c	d	e	f	g

5. Rock Climbing

Starting from the bottom, pick one chunk from each row to translate the sentences below.

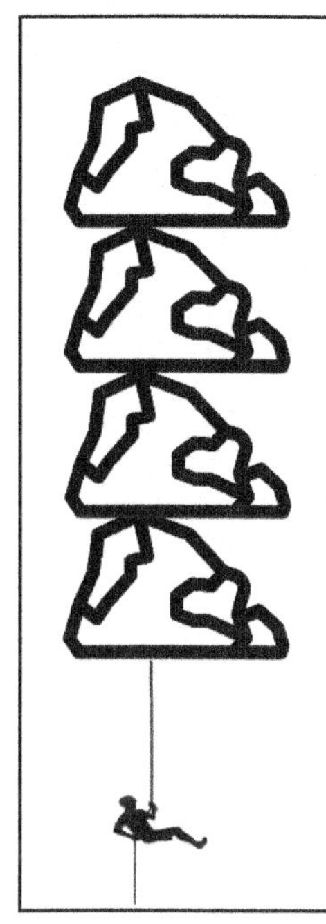

Inglaterra.	francés.	irlandés.	alemán.	inglés.
Hablo	Soy de	y no hablo	y de	pero no hablo
chino	Francia	de inglés	hablas?	eres?
Soy de	Hablo muy bien	¿Qué idiomas	¿De dónde	Hablo un poco
a.	**b.**	**c.**	**d.**	**e.**

a. *I am from France and I don't speak German.*

____

b. *I speak Chinese very well, but I don't speak French.*

____

c. *What languages do you speak? I speak English.*

____

d. *Where are you from? I am from England.*

____

e. *I speak a bit of English and Irish.*

____

6. Mosaic Translation

Use the words in the grid to help you translate the sentences below.

a.	Soy de	hablas?	de francés	muy bien	de chino.
b.	¿De dónde	Italia	Soy	y	Inglaterra.
c.	Hablo	eres?	pero también	de	alemán.
d.	¿Qué idiomas	un poco	Hablo	me gusta	y francés.
e.	Hablo muy bien	inglés	y hablo	italiano	el español.

a. *I am from Italy and I speak Italian and French.*

____

b. *Where are you from? I am from England.*

____

c. *I speak a bit of French and Chinese.*

____

d. *What languages do you speak? I speak German very well.*

____

e. *I speak English very well, but I also like Spanish.*

____

7. Fill in the Gaps

a. Hola, me llamo Roberto. Tengo ________ años. Mi cumpleaños es el veinte ___ junio. Soy de __________ y _________ alemán y ________. También hablo un _______ de inglés.

poco	Italia	ocho	de	francés	hablo

b. Hola, me llamo María. Tengo un perro _______. Soy ____ Francia. Hablo muy _____ alemán y español. ________ hablo ___ poco de francés. Me gusta mucho el ____________.

portugués	un	negro	bien	También	de

8. Tangled Translation

a. Write the Spanish words in English to complete the translation

Hello, **me llamo** Miguel. **Tengo** seven years old. My birthday **es el trece** of March. **Soy** from **Francia.** I speak French and English **muy bien. Yo** also **hablo un poco** Italian, **pero** I don't speak **alemán.** I like **el chino.**

b. Write the English words in Spanish to complete the translation

Buenos días, **my name is** Lorena. **I am** doce años. Mi cumpleaños **is on the 4th** de abril. Tengo **a dog** negro **who is called** Colli. Soy de **Germany. I speak** muy bien inglés **and** hablo **a bit of French,** pero **I don't speak** italiano. **I like** el alemán.

9. Sentence Puzzle

Put the words in each sentence in the correct order

a. muy Hablo inglés francés y bien.

I speak English and French very well.

b. ¿Qué español Hablo idiomas hablas?

What language do you speak? I speak Spanish.

c. ¿De eres? Australia de Soy dónde.

Where are you from? I am from Australia.

d. inglés, Hablo pero hablo no alemán.

I speak English but, I don't speak German.

10. Guided Translation

a. H______, m___ ll__________ M__________. S___ d___ A______________.

Hi, my name is Marta. I am from Australia.

b. S___ d___ E__________. H_________ i___________ m_____ b________.

I am from Spain. I speak Italian very well.

c. H________ f_________ m_____ b_____ y u___ p_____ de i______________.

I speak French very well and I speak Irish a little.

d. H_______ a__________ y f_________, p_______ n___ h_________ c_______.

I speak German and French, but I don't speak Chinese.

e. ¿Q____ i____________ h__________? H_________ c______ y e__________.

What languages do you speak? I speak Chinese and Spanish.

11. Pyramid Translation

Starting from the top, translate each chunk in Spanish. Write the sentences in the box below.

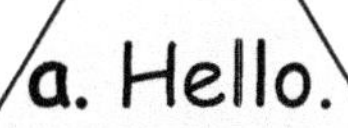

a. Hello.

b. Hello, my name is Claudia.

c. Hello, my name is Claudia. I speak German.

d. Hello, my name is Claudia. I speak German and French.

e. Hello, my name is Claudia. I speak German and French, but I don't speak Chinese.

a.
b.
c.
d.
e.

12. Staircase Translation

Starting from the top, translate each chunk into Spanish.
Write the sentences in the grid below.

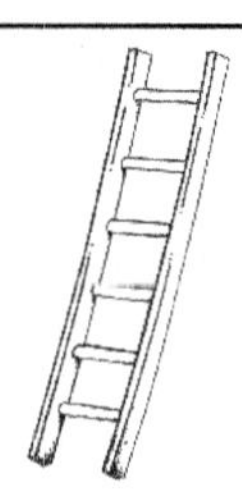

a.	I am from	Ireland.				
b.	I speak	English	and French.			
c.	I do not speak	German,	but I speak	Italian.		
d.	I speak	Chinese	very well,	but I do not speak	Spanish.	
e.	I am from	Scotland.	I speak	a little Portuguese,	but I don't speak	Irish.

Answers / Respuestas

a.	
b.	
c.	
d.	
e.	

Challenge / Desafío

Can you create 2 more sentences using the words in the staircase grid above?

☆	
☆	

UNIT 7 - ¿DE DÓNDE ERES?

LISTENING

1. Split sentences. Listen and match

a. 4   b. 8   c. 2   d. 7   e. 1   f. 3   g. 5   h. 6

2. Faulty Echo

e.g. Soy de ***Argentina****. (dg)*

a. Soy de **China**. (Chaina)
b. Soy de **España.** (Espana)
c. **Hablo** alémán. (Jablo)
d. Soy de **Inglaterra.** (con r- Inglaterror)
e. Hablo inglés y **francés.** (franches)
f. Hablo italiano, pero no hablo **portugués.** (portugués)
g. Hablo **muy** bien chino. (mo-i)

3. Listen and tick the word you hear

a. 2 (No hablo **inglés.)**
b. 3 (Soy de Italia y **hablo** francés.)
c. 2 (Hablo **español** muy bien.)
d. 1 (Soy de **China** y hablo inglés.)
e. 2 (**Soy de** Francia, pero no hablo francés.)

4. Fill in the grid with the correct information in English

a. Ronan ; France ; French
b. Alberto ; Italy ; English (doesn't speak)
c. Pamela ; England ; Spanish
d. Ronaldo ; Portugal ; German

5. Listen and complete with the missing letter

a. Soy d**e** Españ**a**.
b. S**o**y de Francia.
c. Hablo mu**y** bi**e**n inglés.
d. No **h**ablo españo**l**.
e. También habl**o** alemán.
f. ¿Habl**a**s chin**o**? No, hablo galés.
g. S**o**y de China y hablo francés.
h. Habl**o** francés y **u**n poco de italiano.
i. Soy de Port**u**gal y hablo portugu**é**s.
j. ¿Habla**s** italiano? Sí, muy bien.

6. Complete with the missing syllables in the box below

a. **Ha**blo chino.
b. No ha**blo** alemán.
c. Soy de **In**glaterra.
d. Hablo portu**gués.**
e. ¿Hablas in**glés?**
f. Soy de Esco**cia** y hablo inglés.
g. Soy de Fran**cia** y hablo francés.
h. Soy de Espa**ña** y hablo un poco de chino.
i. No hablo muy bien espa**ñol.**
j. Tam**bién** hablo portugués.

7. Can you help the penguin to break the flow? Draw a line between words

a. Hablo inglés y también italiano.
b. Soy de Alemania, pero hablo inglés.
c. Soy de China y hablo un poco de alemán.
d. No hablo irlandés, pero hablo español.
e. Hablo inglés y francés muy bien.
f. ¿Qué idiomas hablas? Hablo chino.

8. Spot the Intruder. Identify the word in each sentence the speaker is NOT saying

a. Hablo inglés, <u>español,</u> pero no soy de Inglaterra. **español**
b. Soy de Australia y <u>no</u> hablo un poco de chino. **no**
c. Hablo alemán, pero <u>también</u> soy italiano. **también**
d. ¿Hablas español? Sí, también <u>soy</u> francés. **soy**
e. No hablo galés, <u>y</u> pero hablo irlandés. **y**
f. Soy de Portugal. Hablo portugués <u>italiano</u>. **italiano**
g. No hablo chino <u>hablas</u> muy bien. **hablas**

9. Catch it, Swap it.
Listen, spot the difference between what you hear and the written text and edit each sentence accordingly.
Transcript:

a. Soy de Italia y hablo muy bien italiano y **chino.** <u>**chino**</u>
b. Soy de Inglaterra y hablo inglés, pero no hablo **francés**. <u>**francés**</u>
c. Soy de **Alemania** y hablo inglés, pero no hablo español. <u>**Alemania**</u>
d. Soy de América y hablo un poco de **portugués**. <u>**portugués**</u>
e. Soy de Escocia y hablo **muy bien** alemán. <u>**muy bien**</u>
f. Soy de **Inglaterra**, pero no hablo muy bien inglés. <u>**Inglaterra**</u>

10. Sentence Bingo: write 4 of the sentences into the grid. You will hear sentences in Spanish in a RANDOM ORDER. Tick all 4 of your sentences to win!

11. Listening Slalom

a. Me llamo Stefano, Soy de Italia, pero hablo portugués. b. Hola, hablo español, pero soy de Alemania.
c. Soy de España y hablo un poco de francés. d. Hablo un poco de chino, pero no hablo inglés.
e. No hablas muy bien irlandés, pero hablas italiano. f. No soy de Inglaterra. Soy de Argentina y hablo español

READING

1. Sylla-Bees

a. **Tengo nueve años, soy** de **Francia** y **hablo chino.** b. **Soy** de **Italia, pero** no **hablo** muy **bien italiano.**

2. True or False

A. Read the paragraphs below and answer True or False

a. True b. False (dog) c. False (English and French) d. True e. True f. False (he likes it)
g. False (Italian) h. False (very well) i. True j. False (she likes speaking in Spanish)

B. Find in the text above the Spanish for:

a. Tiene un año. b. Es muy buena. c. No tengo mascotas.
d. Me gusta mucho. e. Me gusta hablar. f. No me gusta nada.

3. Tick or Cross

A. Read the text. Tick the box if you find the words in the text, cross it if you do not find them

a. X b. X c. X d. X e. ✓ f. X g. X h. X i. ✓ j. X k. ✓ l. ✓

B. Find the Spanish in the text above

a. El quince de octubre. b. No hablo chino. c. Hablo muy bien inglés.
d. Me gusta mucho el alemán. e. No me gusta nada el español.

4. Language Detective

A. Find someone who...

a. Martina b. Martina c. Carmen d. Carmen / Martina e. Ricardo. f. Ricardo / Carmen g. Carmen

B. Odd one out

I don't like Spanish (odd chunk)

WRITING

1. Spelling

a. **Alemán** b. **Un poco** c. **Alemania** d. **Inglaterra** e. **Inglés** f. **Hablo español** g. No **hablo chino**

2. Anagrams
a. Hablo español. b. Soy de Inglaterra. c. No hablo alemán. d. Me gusta el galés. e. Hablo portugués.

3. Gapped Translation
a. I speak **German** and **French,** but I don't speak **English.** b. I am from **Germany** and I speak Irish **very well.**
c. I am from **England** but I don't speak **English.** d. What **languages** do you **speak**? I speak **Irish.**

4. Split Sentences
a. 4 b. 2 c. 5 d 3 e. 6 f. 1 g. 7

5. Rock Climbing
a. Soy de Francia y no hablo alemán. b. Hablo muy bien chino, pero no hablo francés.
c. ¿Qué idiomas hablas? Hablo inglés. d. ¿De dónde eres? Soy de Inglaterra.
e. Hablo un poco de inglés y de irlandés.

6. Mosaic Translation
a. Soy de Italia y hablo italiano y francés. b. ¿De dónde eres? Soy de Inglaterra.
c. Hablo un poco de francés y chino. d. ¿Qué idiomas hablas? Hablo muy bien alemán.
e. Hablo muy bien inglés, pero también me gusta el español.

7. Fill in the Gaps
a. Hola, me llamo Roberto. Tengo **ocho** años. Mi cumpleaños es el veinte **de** junio. Soy de **Italia** y **hablo** alemán y **francés.** También hablo un **poco** de inglés.
b. Hola, me llamo María. Tengo un perro **negro**. Soy **de** Francia. Hablo muy **bien** alemán y español. **También** hablo **un** poco de francés. Me gusta mucho el **portugués**.

8. Tangled Translation
a. Hello, **my name is** Miguel. **I am** seven years old. My birthday **is on the 13th** of March. **I am** from **France.** I speak French and English **very well. I** also **speak a little** Italian, **but** I don't speak **German.** I like **Chinese.**
b. Buenos días, **me llamo** Lorena. **Tengo** doce años. Mi cumpleaños **es el cuatro** de abril. Tengo **un perro** negro **que se llama** Colli. Soy de **Alemania. Hablo** muy bien inglés **y** hablo **un poco de francés,** pero **no hablo** italiano. **Me gusta** el alemán.

9. Sentence Puzzle
a. Hablo inglés y francés muy bien. b. ¿Qué idiomas hablas? Hablo españo.
c. ¿De dónde eres? Soy de Australia. d. Hablo inglés, pero no hablo alemán.

10. Guided Translation
a. **Hola** me **llamo Marta**. **Soy** de **Australia.** b. **Soy** de **España. Hablo italiano** muy **bien.**
c. **Hablo francés** muy **bien** y **un poco** de **irlandés.** d. **Hablo alemán** y **francés, pero** no **hablo chino.**
d. **¿Qué idiomas hablas? Hablo chino** y **español.**

11. Pyramid Translation
Hola, me llamo Claudia. Hablo alemán y francés, pero no hablo chino.

12. Staircase Translation
a. Soy de Irlanda. b. Hablo inglés y francés. c. No hablo alemán, pero hablo italiano. d. Hablo muy bien chino, pero no hablo español. e. Soy de Escocia. Hablo un poco de portugués, pero no hablo irlandés.

UNIT 8
¿QUÉ TIEMPO HACE?

In this unit you will learn how to:

- ✓ Understand and use weather expressions
- ✓ Use time frames and seasons
- ✓ Use *hoy/ hay/ hace*
- ✓ Find a place on the map

You will revisit:

- ★ Countries, languages and nationalities
- ★ Names of Spanish locations

¿Qué tiempo hace hoy?

Hoy hace sol

Unit 8. THE WEATHER

I can describe what the weather is like.

¿Qué tiempo hace? *What is the weather like?*

En invierno *In winter*	hace calor *it is hot*	en Alicante
En otoño *In autumn*	hace frío *it is cold*	en Barcelona
En primavera *In spring*	hace sol *it is sunny*	en Bilbao
En verano *In summer*	hace buen tiempo *it is good weather*	en Ibiza
Esta semana *This week*	hace mal tiempo *it is bad weather*	en Madrid
Hoy *Today*	hace viento *it is windy*	en Mallorca
Normalmente *Normally*	hay niebla *it is foggy*	en Santander
Por lo general *Usually*	hay nubes *it is cloudy*	en Sevilla
	hay tormentas *there are storms*	en Tenerife
	llueve *it rains*	en Valencia
	nieva *it snows*	

Unit 8. What the weather is like: LISTENING

1. Listen and tick the word you hear ✓

	1	2	3
a.	Hace sol	Hace frío	Hace calor
b.	Hay tormentas	Hay viento	Hay niebla
c.	Nieva	Hay niebla	Llueve
d.	Hace buen tiempo	Hace mal tiempo	¿Qué tiempo hace?
e.	Hay tormentas	Hay nubes	Hay viento

2. Faulty Echo

e.g. Hoy hace sol.

a. En invierno hace frío.

b. Normalmente llueve.

c. En verano hace calor.

d. Hoy hay tormentas.

e. Por lo general hace buen tiempo.

f. ¿Qué tiempo hace?

g. Esta semana hay niebla.

3. Listen and Match

a. Today — 1.

b. Normally — 2.

c. In summer — 3.

d. In autumn — 4.

e. In winter — 5.

f. This week — 6.

g. In spring — 7.

a	b	c	d	e	f	g

4. Listen and complete with the missing letter

a. Ha__e frío.

b. Ha__e viento.

c. H__y llueve.

d. __ay tormentas.

e. __ace calor.

f. Hac__ sol.

g. Ho__ nieva.

h. H__ce mal tiempo.

i. H__y nubes.

hace

hay

hoy

5. Listen and complete with the missing letters

a. En primavera llu __ __ __.

b. Hoy hace b __ __ __ tiempo.

c. En otoño hace f__ __ __.

d. En invierno __ __ __va.

e. Por lo __ __ __ __ __ral hace sol.

f. En verano ha __ __ calor.

g. Normalmente h __ __ niebla.

ce	ay	río	gene	nie	eve	uen

6. Can you help the penguin to break the flow?

7. Complete with the missing syllables in the box below

a. En Valencia hace buen _ _ _ _ po.

b. En Santander ha_ _ sol.

c. En Bilbao llue _ _.

d. En Ibiza hace _ _ _ tiempo.

e. En Tenerife hay _ _ bes.

f. En Barcelona hace _ _ _ _ to.

g. En Madrid nie_ _.

h. En Alicante hace _ _ _ o.

i. En Sevilla hay tor_ _ _ tas.

j. En Mallorca hace _ _ lor.

tiem	mal	ce	ve	nu	va	vien	men	frí	ca

8. Fill in the grid with the correct information in English

	When	Weather
a.		
b.		
c.		
d.		
e.		
f.		

9. Spot the Intruder

Identify the word in each sentence the speaker is NOT saying

a. ¿Qué no tiempo hace en Madrid?

b. En Ibiza hay hace buen tiempo.

c. En Barcelona cómo hace mal tiempo.

d. Hoy en Mallorca tengo hay nubes.

e. En Valencia hace es viento.

f. En invierno calor llueve en Bilbao.

10. Listening Slalom

Listen in Spanish and pick the 3 equivalent English parts from each column.

e.g. Hoy hace calor en Valencia.

You could colour each sentence in a different colour. Then, read the sentence out loud.

e.g.	*Today*	there are storms	in Ibiza.
a.	Normally	*it is hot*	in Alicante.
b.	In spring	it is bad weather	*in Valencia.*
c.	In autumn	it is cold	in Barcelona.
d.	Today	it is good weather	in Madrid.
e.	Usually	it rains	in Santander.
f.	This week	it snows	in Seville.
g.	Today	it is sunny	in Tenerife.

Unit 8. What the weather is like: READING

1. Sylla-Bees

Read and put the syllables in the cells in the correct order

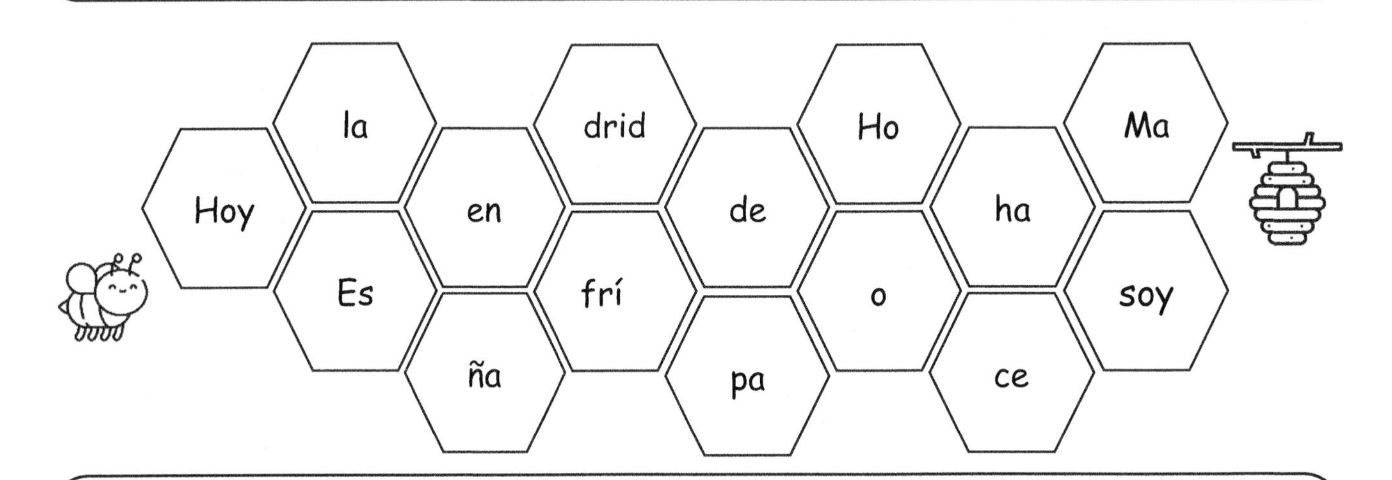

a. Hello, I am from Spain. Today in Madrid it is cold.

H______, s___ d__ E__________. H_____ e__ M________
h_____ f_______.

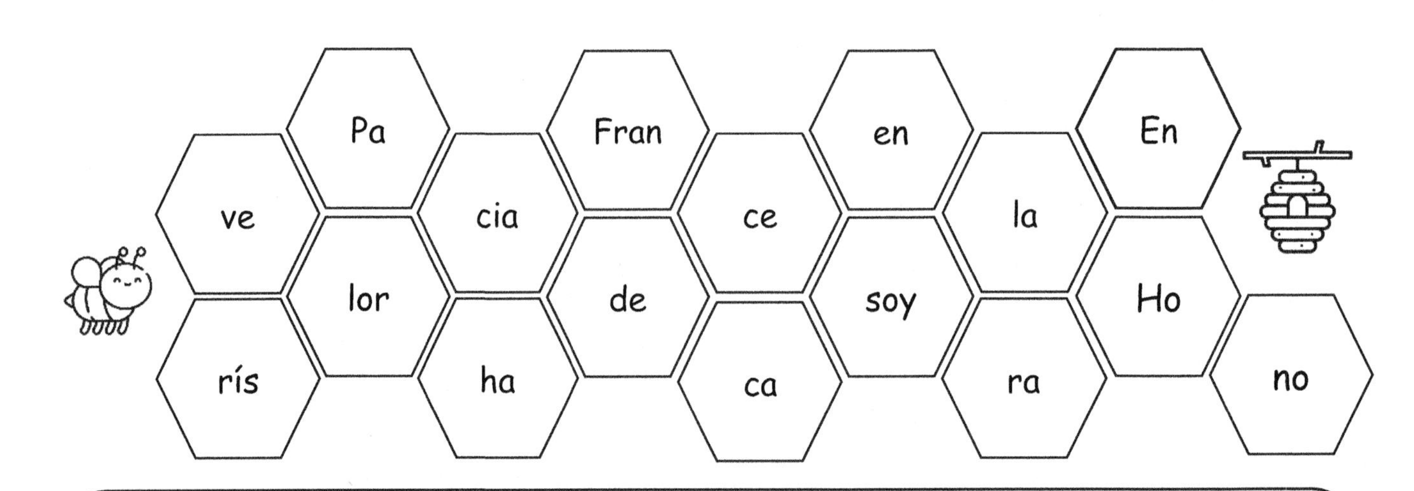

b. Hello, I am from France. In summer in Paris it is hot.

H_______, s___ d__ F___________. E__ v_______ e__
P__________ h_______ c_________.

2. True or False?
Look at the map and for each sentence tick True or False

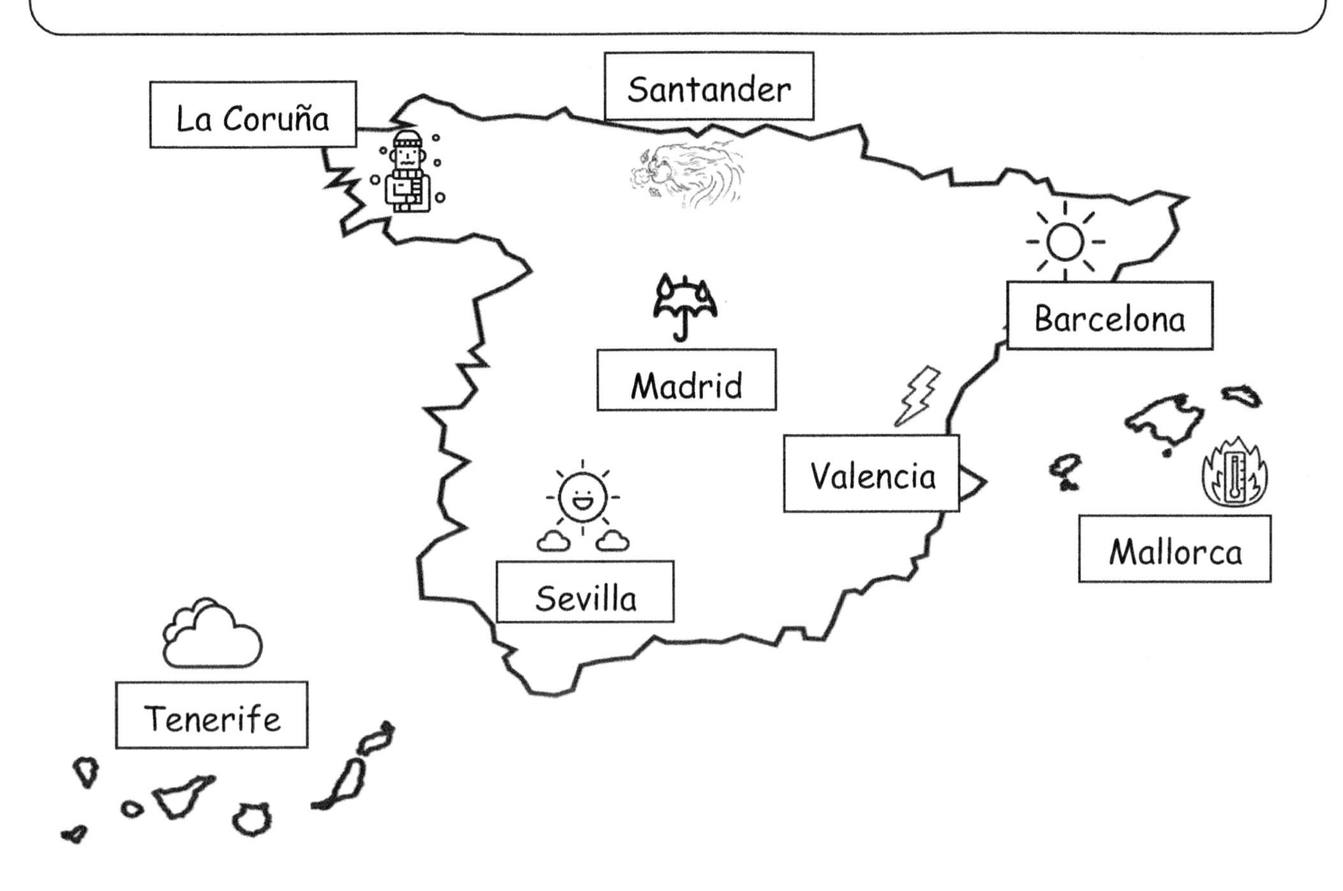

a. Hoy en Tenerife hace calor.
b. Normalmente en Sevilla hace buen tiempo.
c. En Mallorca hace frío.
d. Hoy en Barcelona hace sol.
e. Esta semana en Madrid nieva.
f. Normalmente en Santander hace viento.
g. Hoy en Valencia hay tormentas.
h. Esta semana llueve en La Coruña.

	True	False
a.		
b.		
c.		
d.		
e.		
f.		
g.		
h.		

3. Read, Match, Find and Colour

A. Match these sentences to the pictures above

a. Esta semana nieva en Madrid.
b. Normalmente hace sol en Ibiza.
c. Hoy hay tormentas en Bilbao.
d. En invierno llueve en Alicante.
e. En otoño hay viento en Mallorca.
f. En primavera hace buen tiempo.
g. Por lo general hay nubes en Tenerife.
h. En verano hace calor en Valencia.
i. Hoy hace mal tiempo en Santander.
j. Esta semana hace frío en Sevilla.

B. Using the sentences in task A find the Spanish for:

a. It is hot.
b. It is cloudy.
c. In winter.
d. It is good weather.
e. This week.
f. It is cold.
g. It rains.
h. Today.
i. It is sunny.
j. It is windy.

4. True of False?

A. Read the paragraphs below and then answer True or False

Hola, me llamo **David**. Tengo diez años. Soy de Francia y hablo muy bien francés. En Francia normalmente hace calor, pero hoy no hace buen tiempo, hace frío y llueve.

Hola, me llamo **Paula**. Tengo catorce años. Soy de Alemania y hablo muy bien inglés y chino. En Alemania, por lo general, hace mal tiempo, pero hoy hace sol y hace calor.

	True	False
a. **David** is fourteen years old.		
b. He speaks French very well.		
c. He lives in Germany.		
d. It is normally warm in France.		
e. It is normally cold in France.		
f. It is raining in France today.		
g. **Paula** is French.		
h. In Germany there is usually bad weather.		
i. She speaks German very well.		
j. It is warm in Germany today.		

B. Find in the texts above the Spanish for:

a. But today.

b. It is normally warm.

c. In Germany it is generally bad weather.

d. But the weather is not good today.

5. Language Detective

- Me llamo **Pedro**. Mi cumpleaños es el doce de diciembre. Soy de Irlanda y hablo inglés y francés, pero no hablo chino. En Edimburgo, por lo general, en invierno hay tormentas, pero hoy hace calor y no llueve.

- Me llamo **Carmen**. Mi cumpleaños es el once de diciembre. Soy de España y hablo español. También hablo un poco de italiano. En Madrid en verano siempre hace buen tiempo, pero hoy hay nubes y hace un poco de viento.

- Hola, me llamo **Daniel**. Tengo doce años. Mi cumpleaños es el trece de diciembre. Vivo en Italia. En Roma en primavera normalmente hace buen tiempo, pero hoy llueve y hace frío. No me gusta cuando hace frío.

A. Read & answer the questions

a. Who lives in Italy?

b. Who doesn't speak Chinese?

c. Where isn't it raining today?

d. Where is it raining today?

e. Where is the weather usually good?

f. Who doesn't speak Italian?

g. Where is it cloudy today?

B. Put a cross in the box and underline the corresponding Spanish translation. Two are odd.

I am from Ireland. (X)	I speak English and French.	I have a white and grey cat.
I am from England.	I don't like when it is cold.	I speak Italian a little.
But it rains today.	My birthday is on the 11th of December.	It is a bit windy.
But it is cloudy today.	My birthday is on the 12th of December.	It is warm today.

Unit 8. What the weather is like: WRITING

1. Spelling

a. E__ p_____ a______. *In spring.*

b. E__ i_________ n___. *In winter.*

c. H_____ c____ o__. *It's warm.*

d. E__ ______ ñ__. *In autumn.*

e. __ l______. *It rains.*

f. E__ o_____ o h___ n_____ s. *In autumn it's cloudy.*

g. E__ v_______ o h__ c__ c__ l___. *In summer it is warm.*

2. Gapped Translation

a. Soy de Australia y hoy hace buen tiempo.

I am ______ Australia and it is ________ weather _________.

b. En otoño hace viento en Nueva York.

In ________ it is _______ in _______ York.

c. Soy de Inglaterra y por lo general no hace buen tiempo.

I ___ from England and ____________ it is not _______ weather.

d. Soy de Escocia y normalmente hace mal tiempo.

I am from ____________ and ________ it is _______ weather.

e. Hoy hay nubes y hace viento, pero no hay tormentas.

It is _______ and it is _______, but there are no _________ today.

3. Fill in the gaps

a. Hola, me llamo Carlos. Tengo ________ años. Soy ___ Inglaterra. En Londres, por lo _________ hace ________ y ______ frío, _______ hoy hace calor.

pero	viento	catorce	de	general	hace

b. Hola, ___ llamo Julia. Soy de Italia y ________ diez años. _____ Italia en _________ hace ________ tiempo, pero hoy llueve y hay __________.

tengo	me	verano	buen	nubes	En

4. Sentence Puzzle

Put the words in the correct order

a. España hace tiempo buen En.

It is good weather in Spain.

b. Inglaterra En hace tiempo mal llueve y.

In England it is bad weather and it rains.

c. ¿Qué hace Italia? tiempo en.

What is the weather like in Italy?

d. Hoy y viento, hay llueve hace tormentas no pero.

It rains and it is windy, but there are no storms today.

No Snakes No Ladders

SALIDA	1 Soy de	2 Soy de España	3 Hablo español	4 Soy de Ingla-terra	5 No hablo	6 No hablo galés	7 Hace calor
15 Pero no hablo	14 ¿De dónde eres?	13 Soy de China	12 Hoy hay niebla	11 Hace frío	10 Hablo francés	9 En verano	8 ¿Qué tiempo hace?
16 Hace viento	17 Hace buen tiempo	18 En invierno	19 En primavera	20 ¿Qué idiomas hablas?	21 Hablo inglés	22 Soy de Alemania	23 Un poco de italiano
LLEGADA	30 Nieva en Bilbao	29 Hablo muy bien alemán	28 Hace sol en Alicante	27 Hay nubes en Tenerife	26 Llueve en Madrid	25 Esta semana	24 Hay tormen-tas

No Snakes No Ladders

Unit 7-8

 SALIDA	1 I am from	2 I am from Spain	3 I speak Spanish	4 I am from England	5 I don't speak	6 I don't speak Welsh	7 It is hot
15 But I don't speak	14 Where are you from?	13 I am from China	12 Today it is foggy	11 It is cold	10 I speak French	9 In summer	8 What is the weather like?
16 It is windy	17 It is good weather	18 In winter	19 In spring	20 What languages do you speak?	21 I speak English	22 I am from Germany	23 A little Italian
LLEGADA	30 It snows in Bilbao	29 I speak German very well	28 It is sunny in Alicante	27 It is cloudy in Tenerife	26 It rains in Madrid	25 This week	24 There are storms

UNIT 8 - ¿QUÉ TIEMPO HACE?

LISTENING

1. Listen and tick the word you hear

a. 2 (**Hace frío** en Madrid.) b. 1 (Hoy **hay tormentas.**) c. 3 (**Llueve** en Barcelona.)
d. 1 (**Hace buen tiempo** en Santander.) e. 2 (Esta semana **hay nubes.**)

2. Faulty echo

e.g. ***Hoy*** *hace sol. (H like j)*
a. En invierno **hace** frío. (haze)
b. Normalmente **llueve.** (lueve)
c. En **verano** hace calor. (virano)
d. Hoy **hay** tormentas. (hei)
e. Por lo **general** hace buen tiempo. (g like gato)
f. ¿Qué **tiempo** hace? (tempo)
g. Esta semana hay **niebla**. (naibla)

3. Listen and Match - Transcript

a. Hoy hace calor
b. Normalmente llueve
c. En verano hace sol
d. En otoño hay nubes
e. En invierno nieva
f. Esta semana hay tormentas
g. En primavera hace viento

Answer Key:

a. 3 b. 5 c. 2 d. 4 e. 1 f. 7 g. 6

4. Listen and complete the missing letter

a. El lunes hace frío.
b. El viernes hace viento.
c. Hoy llueve.
d. H**a**y tormentas.
e. El sábado **h**ace calor.
f. El miércoles hac**e** sol.
g. Hoy nieva.
h. El jueves h**a**ce mal tiempo.
i. Hoy h**a**y nubes.

5. Listen and complete with the missing syllable

a. En primavera llu**eve.**
b. Hoy hace b**uen** tiempo.
c. En otoño hace **frío.**
d. En invierno **nie**va.
e. Por lo **gene**ral hace sol.
f. En verano ha**ce** calor.
g. Normalmente h**ay** niebla.

6. Can you help the penguin to break the flow? Draw a line between words

a. ¿Que tiempo hace hoy? Hace sol.
b. En verano hace calor en Madrid.
c. En otoño hace buen tiempo en Barcelona.
d. En invierno hace frío en Santander.
e. Por lo general hay nubes en Tenerife.
f. Hoy hace viento y llueve en Valencia.

7. Complete with the missing syllables in the box below

a. En Valencia hace buen **tiem**po.
b. En Santander ha**ce** sol.
c. En Bilbao llue**ve.**
d. En Ibiza hace **mal** tiempo.
e. En Tenerife hay **nu**bes.
f. En Barcelona hace **vien**to.
g. En Madrid nie**va.**
h. En Alicante hace **frí**o.
i. En Sevilla hay tor**men**tas.
j. En Mallorca hace **ca**lor.

8. Fill in the grid with the correct information in English

a. Normally ; It is good weather
b. In the winter ; It is foggy
c. In the spring ; It rains
d. Today ; It is hot
e. Usually ; It is sunny
f. This week ; It is cold

9 Spot the Intruder

a. ¿Qué no tiempo hace en Madrid? — **no**
b. En Ibiza hay hace buen tiempo — **hay**
c. En Barcelona cómo hace mal tiempo — **cómo**
d. Hoy en Mallorca tengo hay nubes — **tengo**
e. En Valencia hace es viento — **es**
f. En invierno calor llueve en Bilbao — **calor**

10. Listening Slalom

e.g. *Hoy hace calor en Valencia.* *[Today it is hot in Valencia.]*
a. Normalmente hace buen tiempo en Barcelona. [Normally it is good weather in Barcelona.]
b. En primavera llueve en Alicante. [In spring it rains in Alicante.]
c. En otoño hace mal tiempo en Sevilla. [In autumn it is bad weather in Seville.]
d. Hoy hace frío en Santander. [Today it is cold in Santander.]
e. Por lo general hace sol en Ibiza. [Usually it is sunny in Ibiza.]
f. Esta semana hay tormentas en Tenerife. [This week there are storms in Tenerife.]
g. Hoy nieva en Madrid. [Today it snows in Madrid.]

READING

1. Sylla-Bees

a. Hola, soy de España. Hoy en Madrid hace frío.
b. Hola, soy de Francia. En verano en París hace calor.

2. True or False (map)

a. False b. True c. False d. True e. False f. True g. True h. False

3. Read, Match, Find and Colour

A. Match the sentences to the pictures above

a. It snows b. It's sunny c. Storm d. It rains e. It's windy f. It's nice weather
g. It's cloudy h. It's hot i. It's bad weather j. It's cold

B. Using the sentences in task A find the Spanish for:

a. Hace calor b. Hay nubes c. En invierno d. Hace buen tiempo e. Esta semana
f. Hace frío g. Llueve h. Hoy i. Hace sol j. Hace viento

4. True or False

A. Read the paragraphs below and answer True or False

a. False (10) b. True c. False (He is from France) d. True e. False (it is warm) f. True
g. False (She is from Germany) h. True i. False (She speaks English very well) j. True

B. Find in the texts above the Spanish for:

a. Pero hoy... b. Normalmente hace calor. c. En Alemania por lo general hace mal tiempo.
d. Pero hoy no hace buen tiempo.

5. Language Detective

A. Read & answer the questions

a. Daniel b. Pedro c. In Edinburgh d. In Rome e. In Rome f. Pedro g. In Madrid

B. Odd two out

I am from England / I have a white and grey cat (odd ones)

WRITING

1. Spelling

a. **En primavera** b. **En invierno** c. **Hace calor.** d. **En otoño** e. **Llueve.**
f. **En otoño hay nubes.** g. **En verano hace calor.**

2. Gapped Translation

a. I am **from** Australia and it is **good** weather **today.**
b. In **autumn** it is **windy** in **New** York.
c. I **am** from England and **generally** it is not **good** weather.
d. I am from **Scotland** and **usually** it is **bad** weather.
e. It is **cloudy** and it is **windy,** but there are no **storms** today.

3. Fill in the gaps

a. Hola, me llamo Carlos. Tengo **catorce** años. Soy **de** Inglaterra. En Londres, por lo **general** hace **viento** y **hace** frío, **pero** hoy hace calor.
b. Hola, **me** llamo Julia. Soy de Italia y **tengo** diez años. **En** Italia en **verano** hace **buen** tiempo, pero hoy llueve y hay **nubes.**

4. Sentence Puzzle

a. En España hace buen tiempo. b. En Inglaterra hace mal tiempo y llueve.
c. ¿Qué tiempo hace en Italia? d. Hoy llueve y hace viento, pero no hay tormentas.

UNIT 9

MI CIUDAD

In this unit you will learn how to say in Spanish:

- ✓ Where you live
- ✓ Say if you like/ dislike your town and why
- ✓ Use *vivo/vives*

You will revisit:

- ★ How to use *me encanta/me gusta/no gusta/odio*
- ★ Masculine/ feminine adjectival agreement
- ★ Word order noun + adjective

Vivo en Barcelona

Me encanta mi ciudad porque es bonita

UNIT 9. MI CIUDAD
I can talk about where I live

¿Dónde vives? *Where do you live?*
¿Te gusta tu ciudad? *Do you like your city?*

<table>
<tr>
<td rowspan="2">Vivo en
I live in</td>
<td rowspan="2">Barcelona

Edimburgo
Edinburgh

Harrogate

Leeds

Londres
London

Madrid

Marbella

Nueva York
New York

Roma
Rome

Ronda

Sidney</td>
<td rowspan="2">Me encanta
I love

Me gusta
I like

No me gusta
I don't like

Odio
I hate</td>
<td>mi pueblo
my town</td>
<td rowspan="2">porque es
because it is

porque no es
because it is not</td>
<td>animado *lively*
bonito *pretty*
feo *ugly*
grande *big*
pequeño *small*
ruidoso *noisy*
tranquilo *quiet*
turístico *touristic*</td>
</tr>
<tr>
<td>mi ciudad
my city</td>
<td>animada *lively*
bonita *pretty*
fea *ugly*
pequeña *small*
ruidosa *noisy*
tranquila *quiet*
turística *touristic*</td>
</tr>
</table>

Unit 9: Where I live: LISTENING

1. Listen and tick the word you hear

	1	2	3
a.	Londres	vivo	pueblo
b.	me gusta	ciudad	bonito
c.	bonita	pueblo	odio
d.	animada	ruidosa	grande
e.	me encanta	tranquilo	vivo

2. Faulty Echo

e.g. Vivo en Barcelona.

a. Me gusta mi pueblo.

b. Me encanta mi ciudad.

c. No me gusta mi ciudad.

d. Vivo en Londres.

e. Mi pueblo es pequeño.

f. Mi ciudad es fea.

g. Porque es ruidosa.

h. Porque es tranquilo.

3. Listen and complete with the missing letters

a. Vivo __n Nueva York.

b. Mi ci__dad es bonit__.

c. Mi pu__blo es pe__ueño.

d. Viv__ en Edi__burgo.

e. M__ ciudad es tranquil__.

f. Mi pueblo es bonit__.

g. Mi puebl__ es tranquil__.

h. M__ gusta m__ ciudad.

i. No me g__sta mi pue__lo.

j. Mi ciuda__ es peque__a.

4. Narrow Listening. Gap-fill

a. Hola, me llamo Fernando y tengo once ________. Soy de ________________, pero vivo _____ Inglaterra. Hablo un ________ de inglés y hablo muy _________ irlandés y ________________. Me gusta mi _____________ porque es tranquilo y ________________.

español	en	bien	Irlanda	pueblo	años	poco	bonito

b. Hola, me llamo Rosa y tengo _________ años. Soy ___ España, pero _______ en Alemania. Hablo__________, español y __________. Me encanta mi __________ porque ___ grande, pero ___________.

vivo	alemán	once	ciudad	ruidosa	es	de	francés

5. Fill in the grid with the correct information in English

		☺ Opinion ☹	Reason (Adjective)
a.	Ernesto		
b.	Antonio		
c.	Stefano		
d.	Carlota		
e.	Miguel		
f.	Gianfranco		

6. Complete with the missing syllables in the box below

a. Vivo _ _ Madrid.

b. _ _ gusta mi pueblo.

c. Me gusta _ _ ciudad.

d. O _ _ _ mi ciudad.

e. Me en _ _ _ ta mi pueblo.

f. _ _ me gusta mi pueblo.

g. Mi ciudad _ _ fea.

h. Mi _ _ _ blo es feo.

i. ¿ _ _ gusta tu pueblo?

j. Mi pueblo es _ _ _ doso.

can	te	pue	rui	en	me	es	mi	dio	no

7. Spot the Intruder

Identify the word in each sentence the speaker is NOT saying

a. Vivo en Londres. Me gusta mi ciudad porque no es bonita.

b. Vivo en Ronda. No me gusta mi me pueblo porque es pequeño.

c. Vivo en Roma y odio mi ciudad porque es muy ruidosa.

d. Me encanta mi ciudad porque es grande, bonita y animada.

e. No me gusta mi me ciudad porque es tranquila.

f. ¿Dónde vives? Vivo a en Nueva York. Me encanta porque es grande.

g. Me gusta mi pueblo porque donde es turístico.

h. Mi no me gusta Leeds porque es fea.

8. Catch it, Swap it.

Listen, spot the difference between what you hear and the written text and edit each sentence accordingly

e.g. Me gusta mi ciudad porque no es bonita.	*tranquila*
a. No me gusta mi pueblo porque es pequeño.	
b. Odio mi ciudad porque es muy grande.	
c. Me encanta mi ciudad porque es tranquila.	
d. No me gusta mi ciudad porque es ruidosa.	
e. No me gusta mi ciudad porque es fea.	
f. Me gusta mi pueblo porque es tranquilo.	
g. Me encanta Nueva York porque es animada.	

9. Sentence bingo

Write 4 of the sentences into the grid. You will hear sentences in Spanish in a RANDOM ORDER. Tick all 4 of your sentences to win!

1. No me gusta mi pueblo porque es pequeño.
2. No me gusta mi pueblo porque es feo.
3. Me gusta mi pueblo porque es tranquilo.
4. Me encanta mi ciudad porque es tranquila.
5. Odio mi ciudad porque es muy grande.
6. Me gusta mi ciudad porque no es bonita.
7. No me gusta mi ciudad porque es horrible.
8. Me gusta mi ciudad porque es grande.
9. Odio mi ciudad porque es fea.
10. Me encanta Nueva York porque es animada.

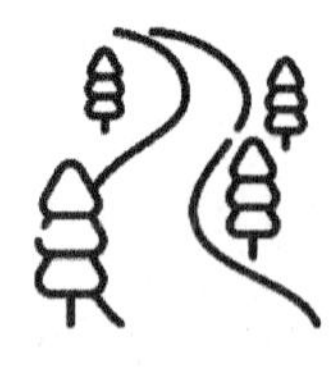

10. Listening Slalom

Listen in Spanish and pick the equivalent English words from each column.

e.g. Me llamo Juan, vivo en Madrid. Me encanta mi ciudad.

Colour in the boxes for each sentence in a different colour.

e.g.	***My name is Juan***	because it is pretty	lively and touristic.
a.	I live in New York	***I live in Madrid***	and quiet.
b.	I live in Marbella	I love my city	***I love my city.***
c.	I don't like	It is big	because it is lively.
d.	I like my town	I like my town	and big.
e.	I hate my city	my town because	because is touristic.
f.	I live in London	because it is ugly	it is small.

Unit 9: Where I live: READING

1. Read and put the syllables in the cells in the correct order

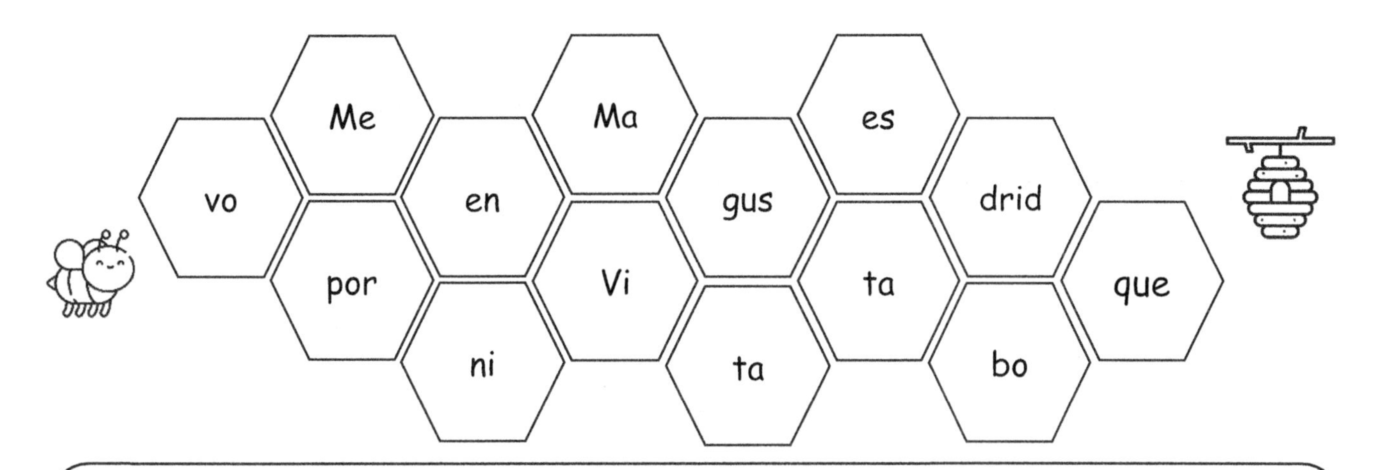

a. I live in Madrid. I like it because it is pretty.

V_______ e__ M_________. M__ g__________ p________ e__ b__________.

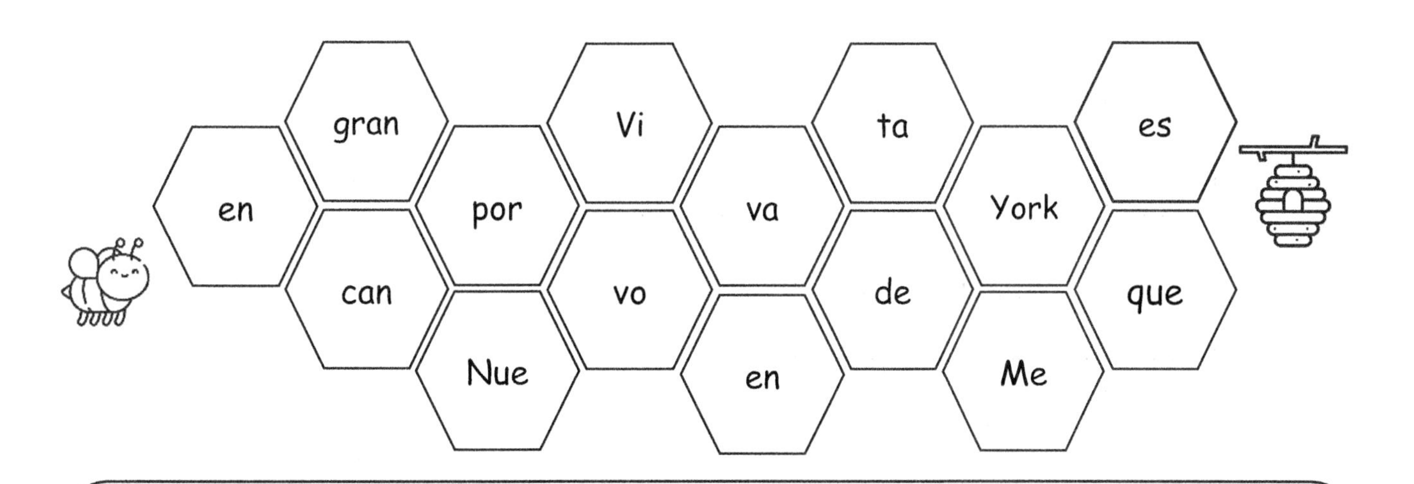

b. I live in New York. I love it because it is big.

V______ e__ N________ Y________. M__ e____________ p___________ e__ g__________.

2. True or False

A. Read the paragraphs below and then answer True or False

Hola, me llamo **Mario**. Tengo cinco años. Soy de Francia y hablo muy bien inglés. En Francia normalmente hace calor. Vivo en París. Me gusta mi ciudad porque es grande y turística.

Hola, me llamo **Pilar**. Tengo once años. Soy de Alemania y hablo alemán y francés. En Alemania, por lo general, hace frío. Vivo en Harrogate, en Inglaterra. Me encanta mi pueblo porque es pequeño y bonito. También es turístico.

	True	False
a. **Mario** is 15 years old.		
b. He speaks very well French.		
c. He lives in Paris.		
d. It is normally cold in France.		
e. He likes his city.		
f. His city is big and lively.		
g. **Pilar** is German.		
h. It is generally cold in Germany.		
i. She lives in Germany.		
j. She likes her town because it is calm.		

B. Find in the texts above the Spanish for:

a. It is normally warm. b. It is small and pretty. c. I love it.

d. It is generally cold. e. It is big and touristic. f. I live in Paris.

3. Tick or Cross

A. Read the texts. Tick the box if you find the words in the text, cross it if you do not find them.

- Hola, me llamo **Patricia.**

Tengo diez años. Soy de España y hablo muy bien español y alemán. Vivo en Barcelona. Hoy en Barcelona llueve. Me gusta mi ciudad porque es animada, pero es muy ruidosa.

- Hola, me llamo **Pablo.**

Tengo siete años. Soy de Italia y hablo muy bien italiano, pero no hablo francés. Vivo en Roma. En Roma normalmente hace sol. Odio mi ciudad porque es turística y ruidosa. Prefiero una ciudad tranquila.

	✓	✗
a. Tengo diez años.		
b. Soy de Francia.		
c. Hablo un poco.		
d. Vivo en París.		
e. No me gusta.		
f. Es animada.		

	✓	✗
g. I am 6 years old.		
h. I am from Spain.		
i. I hate my city.		
j. I speak French.		
k. Because it's sunny.		
l. Because it is noisy.		
m. A calm city.		

B. Find the Spanish in the texts above

a. Today in Barcelona it is raining. ______________________

b. I prefer a calm city. ______________________

c. In Rome it is normally sunny. ______________________

d. I hate my city because it is touristic. ______________________

e. Because it is lively, but is very noisy. ______________________

4. Language Detective

- Me llamo **Ricardo**. Mi cumpleaños es el tres de diciembre. No tengo mascotas. Soy de Irlanda, pero vivo en Inglaterra en Londres. Me gusta mi ciudad porque es animada y turística, pero normalmente hace mal tiempo.

- Me llamo **Consuelo.** Tengo trece años. Tengo un perro blanco y negro que se llama Sleepy. Soy de España y vivo en Ronda. Me encanta mi pueblo porque es tranquilo y bonito. Por lo general también hace buen tiempo.

- Hola, me llamo **Daniela.** Tengo once años. Tengo un gato blanco y gris que se llama Júpiter. Soy de Italia, pero vivo en América, en Detroit. No me gusta mi ciudad porque es fea y ruidosa. Hoy en Detroit llueve.

A. Find someone who...

a. ...is 11 years old.

b. ...has a black and white dog.

c. ...lives in a town.

d. ...has a white and grey cat.

e. ...lives in an ugly and noisy place.

f. ...lives in a lively place.

g. ...doesn't own a cat.

B. Put a cross in the box and underline the corresponding Spanish translation. One is odd.

~~I am from Ireland.~~	But I live in America.	I have a white and grey cat.
I don't have any pets.	I like my town.	I have a white and black dog.
Because it is calm and pretty.	I like my city.	It is raining in Detroit today.
Because it is ugly and noisy.	I don't like my city.	The weather is normally good.

Unit 9: Where I live: WRITING

1. Spelling

a. A _ _ _ a _ _ — *Lively*

b. R _ _ _ _ s _ — *Noisy*

c. E _   _ _   p _ _ _ l _. — *In my town.*

d. M_   c _ _ _ _ _ — *My city*

e. P _ _ _ _ ñ _ — *Small*

f. M _   _ _ _ _ _ d   e _   _ _ _ _. — *My city is ugly.*

g. V _ _ _   e _   L _ _ _ r _ _. — *I live in London.*

2. Anagrams

a. oviV ne Epsaañ. — *I live in Spain.*

b. eM ugast dresLon. — *I like London.*

c. oidO im eupolb. — *I hate my town.*

d. oPurqe es namidao. — *Because it is lively.*

3. Gapped Translation

a. Soy de Australia, pero vivo en Escocia.

I am ______ Australia, but I _______ in Scotland.

b. Me gusta mi pueblo porque es muy bonito y grande.

I like my ________ because it is _______ pretty and ________.

c. Vivo en Londres. Me encanta mi ciudad.

I _________ in London. I __________ my __________.

d. ¿Te gusta tu pueblo? No, no me gusta mi pueblo.

Do you like _____ town? No, I don't like _____ town.

e. ¿Dónde vives? Vivo en un pueblo animado, pero pequeño.

Where do ____ _______? I live in a _______ but ________ town.

4. Split Sentences

a. Vivo en
b. No hablo
c. Soy
d. Me gusta
e. Porque
f. Porque es
g. Me encanta mi

1. es bonita.
2. pueblo.
3. mi ciudad.
4. de España.
5. turístico.
6. francés.
7. Francia.

a	b	c	d	e	f	g

5. Rock Climbing

Starting from the bottom, pick one chunk from each row to translate the sentences below.

es pequeño.	en Roma.	fea.	es grande.	en Edimburgo.
Vivo	No, porque	y vivo	porque es	porque
mi ciudad	Inglaterra	tu pueblo?	mi pueblo	vives?
Soy de	No me gusta	¿Te gusta	Me gusta	¿Dónde
a.	b.	c.	d.	e.

a. I am from England and I live in Rome.

____

b. I don't like my city because it is ugly.

____

c. Do you like your town? No, because it is small.

____

d. I like my town because it is big.

____

e. Where do you live? I live in Edinburgh.

____

6. Mosaic Translation
Use the words in the grid to help you translate the sentences below.

a.	Mi ciudad	es bonita	y bonito.	me encanta	pequeño.
b.	¿Dónde	tu ciudad?	y pequeña,	También es	grande.
c.	No me gusta	vives?	Sí,	pero es	turística.
d.	¿Te gusta	mi pueblo	Vivo en	un pueblo	ruidoso.
e.	Mi pueblo	es tranquilo	porque es	feo y	Londres.

a. *My city is pretty and small, but it is touristic.*

____

b. *Where do you live? I live in a big town.*

____

c. *I don't like my town because it is ugly and noisy.*

____

d. *Do you like your city? Yes, I love London.*

____

e. *My town is calm and pretty. It is also small.*

____

7. Fill in the gaps

a. Hola, me llamo Simón. Tengo ________ años. Soy de ________, pero vivo ___ Inglaterra. __________ un poco de alemán. Me gusta mi ____________ porque ___ tranquilo.

en	hablo	doce	es	pueblo	España

b. Hola, me llamo Julia. Soy de Italia, pero _______ en ________. Hablo muy ______ inglés e italiano. También hablo un poco ___ español. Me encanta mi _______ porque es tranquila __ bonita.

ciudad	y	vivo	bien	Glasgow	de

8. Tangled Translation

a. Write the Spanish words in English to complete the translation

Hello, **me llamo** Consuelo. **Soy de** Spain, **pero** I live **en Alemania.** I speak German **y español.** In Germany, **por lo general,** it rains. I live **en Berlín y** I don't like it **porque es** very big and **ruidosa.**

b. Write the English words in Spanish to complete the translation

Buenos días, **my name is** José. Tengo **eleven** años y **I don't have** mascotas. Vivo **in New York.** Me gusta **my city** porque es **very big** y **pretty. Also** me encanta **because** es animada y **it is not** fea. En Nueva York, **normally** hace buen **weather and** hace **warm.**

9. Sentence Puzzle

Put the words in the correct order

a. bonita gusta muy es Me mi ciudad porque.

I like my city because it is very pretty.

b. ¿Dónde Vivo Nueva York en gusta no me y vives?

Where do you live? I live in New York and I don't like it.

c. ¿Te gusta me encanta es pequeño porque tu pueblo?

Do you like your town? I love it because it is small.

d. Londres ruidosa es porque muy Odio turística y también.

I hate London because it is very noisy and also touristic.

10. Guided Translation

a. H______, m___ l__________ P__________. V______ e___ R_________.

Hi, my name is Patricia. I live in Rome.

b. S____ d___ E__________. H_________ m_____ b________ i___________.

I am from Spain. I speak English very well.

c. V_____ e___ u___ p________ b______. M___ g________ p______ e___ t______.

I live in a pretty town. I like it because it is calm.

d. M___ c__________ e___ a_________ y t____________ t______________.

My city is lively and also touristic.

e. ¿D_______ v_______? V_________ e___ N________ Y______.

Where do you live? I live in New York.

11. Pyramid Translation

Starting from the top, translate each chunk in Spanish. Write the sentences in the box below.

a. Hello.

b. Hello, my name is Carlota.

c. Hello, my name is Carlota. I live in London.

d. Hello, my name is Carlota. I live in London. I like my city because it is big and pretty.

e. Hello, my name is Carlota. I live in London. I like my city because it is big and pretty, but it is not touristic.

a.
b.
c.
d.
e.

12. Staircase Translation

Starting from the top, translate each chunk into Spanish. Write the sentences in the grid below.

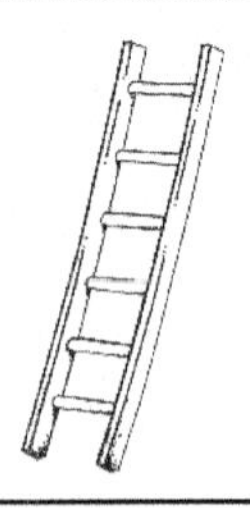

a.	I like	my city.				
b.	I don't like	my town because	it is touristic.			
c.	I love	my town beacuse	it is pretty	and lively.		
d.	I hate	my city because	it is big,	touristic	and also noisy.	
e.	I really like	my town because	it is pretty,	small	and also	quiet.

Answers / Respuestas

a.	
b.	
c.	
d.	
e.	

Challenge / Desafío

Can you create 2 more sentences using the words in the staircase grid above?

☆	
☆	

UNIT 9 - MI CIUDAD

LISTENING

1. Listen and tick the word you hear

a. 1 b. 3 c. 1 d. 2 e. 2

2. Faulty Echo

e.g. Vivo en Barcelona. (in)
a. Me gusta mi **pueblo.** (publo)
b. Me **encanta** mi ciudad. (enchanta)
c. No **me** gusta mi ciudad. (mi)
d. Vivo en **Londres.** (Londcres)
e. Mi pueblo es **pequeño.** (pequino)
f. Mi ciudad es **fea.** (fia)
g. **Porque** es ruidosa. (porqui)
h. Porque es **tranquilo.** (trankuilo)

3. Listen and complete with the missing letter

a. Viv**o** **e**n Nueva York.
b. **Mi** ci**u**dad es bonit**a.**
c. Mi pu**e**blo es pe**q**ueño.
d. Viv**o** en Edi**m**burgo.
e. **Mi** ciudad es tranquil**a.**
f. Mi pueblo es bonit**o.**
g. **Mi** puebl**o** es tranquil**o.**
h. **Me** gusta **mi** ciudad.
i. No me **g**usta mi pueblo.
j. Mi ciuda**d** es peque**ñ**a.

4. Narrow Listening. Gap-fill

a. Hola, me llamo Fernando y tengo once **años.** Soy de **Irlanda,** pero vivo **en** Inglaterra. Hablo un **poco** de inglés y hablo muy **bien** irlandés y **español**. Me gusta mi **pueblo** porque es tranquilo y **bonito**.

b. Hola, me llamo Rosa y tengo **once** años. Soy **de** España, pero **vivo** en Alemania. Hablo **alemán**, español y **francés**. Me encanta mi **ciudad** porque **es** grande, pero **ruidosa**.

5. Fill in the grid with the correct information in English

a. Ernesto ; likes it ; pretty
b. Antonio ; doesn't like it ; small
c. Stefano ; loves it ; lively
d. Carlota ; likes it ; big
e. Miguel ; hates it ; ugly
e. Gianfranco ; loves it ; quiet/calm

6. Complete with the missing syllables in the box below

a. Vivo **en** Madrid.
b. **Me** gusta mi pueblo.
c. Me gusta **mi** ciudad.
d. **Odio** mi ciudad.
e. Me en**can**ta mi pueblo.
f. **No** me gusta mi pueblo.
g. Mi ciudad **es** fea.
h. Mi **pue**blo es feo.
i. ¿**Te** gusta tu pueblo?
j. Mi pueblo es **rui**doso.

7. Spot the Intruder. Identify the word in each sentence the speaker is NOT saying

a. No b. Me c. Muy d. Bonita e. Me f. A g. Donde h. Mi

8. Catch it, Swap it: listen, spot the difference and edit each sentence accordingly

a. **ruidoso** ; pequeño
b. **fea** ; grande
c. **animada** ; tranquila
d. **pequeña** ; ruidosa
e. **fea** ; grande
f. **bonito** ; tranquilo
g. **turística** ; animada

9. Sentence Bingo: write 4 of the sentences into the grid. You will hear sentences in Spanish in a RANDOM ORDER. Tick all 4 of your sentences to win!

1. Odio mi ciudad porque es fea.
2. No me gusta mi pueblo porque es feo.
3. Me gusta mi ciudad porque es bonita.
4. No me gusta mi pueblo porque es pequeño.
5. Odio mi ciudad porque es muy grande.
6. Me encanta mi ciudad porque es tranquila.
7. No me gusta mi ciudad porque es horrible.
8. Me gusta mi ciudad porque es grande.
9. Me gusta mi pueblo porque es tranquilo.
10. Me encanta Nueva York porque es animada.

10. Listening Slalom

e.g. Me llamo Juan, vivo en Madrid. Me encanta mi ciudad.

a. Vivo en Nueva York. Me encanta mi ciudad porque es animada.
b. Vivo en Marbella. Me gusta mi pueblo porque es turístico.
c. No me gusta mi pueblo porque es pequeño.
d. Me gusta mi pueblo porque es bonito y tranquilo.
e. Odio mi ciudad porque es fea y grande.
f. Vivo en Londres. Es grande, animada y turística.

READING

1. Sylla-Bees

a. Vivo en Madrid. Me gusta porque es bonita. b. Vivo en New York. Me encanta porque es grande.

2. True or False

A. Read the paragraphs below and answer True or False

a. False (cinco) b. False (French) c. True d. False (it is warm) e. True f. False (big and touristic) g. True h. True i. False (she lives in England) j. False (small, pretty and touristic)

B. Find in the text above the Spanish for:

a. Normalmente hace calor. b. Es pequeño y bonito. c. Me encanta.
d. Por lo general hace frío. e. Es grande y turística. f. Vivo en París.

3. Tick or Cross

A. Read the text. Tick the box if you find the words in the text, cross it if you do not find them

a. ✓ b. X c. X d. X e. X f. ✓ g. X h. X i. ✓ j. X k. X l. ✓ m. ✓

B. Find the Spanish in the text above

a. Hoy en Barcelona llueve. b. Prefiero una ciudad tranquila.
c. En Roma normalmente hace sol. d. Odio mi ciudad porque es turística.
e. Porque es animada, pero es muy ruidosa.

4. Language Detective

A. Find someone who...

a. Daniela b. Consuelo c. Consuelo d. Daniela e. Daniela f. Ricardo g. Ricardo y Consuelo

B. Odd one out: I like my town. (odd chunk)

WRITING

1. Spelling

a. Animado b. Ruidoso c. En mi pueblo d. Mi ciudad
e. Pequeño f. Mi ciudad es fea g. Vivo en Londres

2. Anagrams

a. Vivo en España. b. Me gusta Londres. c. Odio mi pueblo. d. Porque es animado.

3. Gapped Translation

a. I am **from** Australia but I **live** in Scotland.
b. I like my **town** because it is **very** pretty and **big.**
c. I **live** in London. I **love** my **city.**
d. Do you like **your** town? No, I don't like **my** town.
e. Where do **you live**? I live in a **lively** but **small** town.

4. Split Sentences

a. 7 b. 6 c. 4 d. 3 e. 1 f. 5 g. 2

5. Rock Climbing

a. Soy de Inglaterra, pero vivo en Roma. b. No me gusta mi ciudad porque es fea. c. ¿Te gusta tu pueblo? No, porque es pequeño. d. Me gusta mi pueblo porque es grande. e. ¿Dónde vives? Vivo en Edimburgo.

6. Mosaic Translation

a. Mi ciudad es bonita y pequeña, pero es turística.
b. ¿Dónde vives? Vivo en un pueblo grande.
c. No me gusta mi pueblo porque es feo y ruidoso.
d. ¿Te gusta tu ciudad? Sí, me encanta Londres.
e. Mi pueblo es tranquilo y bonito. También es pequeño.

7. Fill in the Gaps

a. Hola, me llamo Simón. Tengo **doce** años. Soy de **España,** pero vivo **en** Inglaterra. **Hablo** un poco de alemán. Me gusta mi **pueblo** porque **es** tranquilo.
b. Hola, me llamo Julia. Soy de Italia, pero **vivo** en **Glasgow**. Hablo muy **bien** inglés e italiano. También hablo un poco **de** español. Me gusta mi **ciudad** porque es tranquila **y** bonita.

8. Tangled Translation

a. Hello, **my name is** Consuelo. **I am from** Spain, **but** I live **In Germany.** I speak German **and Spanish.** In Germany, **generally,** it rains. I live **in Berlin and** I don't like it **because it is** very big and **noisy.**
b. Buenos días, **me llamo** José. Tengo **once** años y **no tengo** mascotas. Vivo **en Nueva York**. Me gusta **mi ciudad** porque es **muy grande** y **bonita. También** me encanta **porque** es animada y **no es** fea. En Nueva York, **normalmente** hace buen **tiempo y** hace **calor.**

9. Sentence Puzzle

a. Me gusta mi ciudad porque es muy bonita.
b. ¿Dónde vives? Vivo en Nueva York y no me gusta.
c. ¿Te gusta tu pueblo? Me encanta porque es pequeño.
d. Odio Londres porque es ruidosa y también turística.

10. Guided Translation

a. **Hola me llamo Patricia. Vivo en Roma.** b. **Soy de España. Hablo muy bien inglés.** c. **Vivo en un pueblo, me gusta poruqe es tranquilo.** d. **Mi ciudad es animada** y **también turística.** e. **¿Dónde vives? Vivo en Nueva York.**

11. Pyramid Translation

Hola, me llamo Carlota. Vivo en Londres. Me gusta mi ciudad porque es grande y bonita, pero no es turística.

12. Staircase Translation

a. Me gusta mi ciudad.
b. No me gusta mi pueblo porque es turístico.
c. Me encanta mi pueblo porque es bonito y animado.
d. Odio mi ciudad porque es grande y turística también ruidosa.
e. Me gusta mi pueblo porque es bonito y pequeño y no es ruidoso.

UNIT 10
EN MI PUEBLO

In this unit you will learn how to:

- Say what's in your town
- Practise singular and plural nouns

You will revisit:

★ How to use *hay/no hay*
★ *Un/una*
★ Saying where you live
★ Giving your opinion on your town

En mi barrio hay una piscina

En mi pueblo hay restaurantes

Unit 10. I can say what's in my town

¿Qué hay en tu pueblo? *What's in your town?*

		un castillo *a castle*		castillos *castles*
		un cine *a cinema*		cines *cinemas*
		un colegio *a school*		colegios *schools*
		un estadio *a stadium*		estadios *stadiums*
En mi pueblo *In my town*		un museo *a museum*		museos *museums*
		un parque *a park*		parques *parks*
	hay *there is*	un polideportivo *a sports centre*	y *and*	polideportivos *sports centres*
		un restaurante *a restaurant*		restaurantes *restaurants*
En mi ciudad *In my city*		un supermercado *a supermarket*		supermercados *supermarkets*
		una biblioteca *a library*		bibliotecas *libraries*
		una catedral *a cathedral*		catedrales *cathedrals*
	no hay *there is not*	una estación de tren *a train station*		estaciones de tren *train stations*
En mi barrio *In my neighbour-hood*		una farmacia *a pharmacy*	y también *and also*	farmacias *pharmacies*
		una iglesia *a church*		iglesias *churches*
		una panadería *a bakery*		panaderías *bakeries*
		una piscina *a swimming pool*		piscinas *swimming pools*
		una playa *a beach*		playas *beaches*
		una plaza *a square*		plazas *squares*
		una tienda *a shop*		tiendas *shops*

Unit 10. I can say what's in my town: LISTENING

1. Listen and tick the word you hear

	1	2	3
a.	piscina	plaza	estación de tren
b.	cine	ciudad	colegio
c.	hay	no hay	también
d.	tienda	teatro	teatros
e.	estadios	iglesias	en mi pueblo

2. Faulty Echo

You will listen to each sentence twice. The first one is correct, and the second one has an incorrect sound. Underline the wrong word in each sentence.

e.g. En mi pueblo hay un cine.

a. En mi ciudad hay una iglesia.

b. En mi pueblo hay una biblioteca.

c. En mi ciudad hay restaurantes y parques.

d. En mi pueblo no hay piscinas.

e. En mi pueblo hay un polideportivo y un castillo.

f. En mi ciudad hay una plaza, pero no hay un museo.

3. Listen and complete with the missing vowels

a. Mi puebl__

b. Una pl__za

c. Una pisc__na

d. Mi c__udad

e. Un cin__

f. Un m__seo

g. Un polid__portivo

h. Una p__nadería

i. Una __glesia

j. H__y una plaza

a e i o u

4. Complete with the missing syllables in the box below

a. Un supermer _ _do

b. Un tea _ _ _

c. Tien _ _ _

d. Co _ _ gios

e. Un par _ _ _

f. Una far _ _ cia

g. Una bi _ _ _ _ teca

h. Un casti _ _ _

i. Res _ _ _ rantes

j. Mi _ _ _ dad

le	ca	ma	das	que	blio	ciu	tau	tro	llo

5. Fill in the grid with the information in English

	There is *(hay)* ✓	There is not *(no hay)* ✗
e.g.	*a castle*	*a river*
a.		
b.		
c.		
d.		

6. Spot the Intruder

Identify the word in each sentence the speaker is NOT saying

e.g. En mi barrio hay una piscina, <u>iglesia</u> y un polideportivo.

a. En mi pueblo hay restaurantes y un colegios.

b. Me gusta mi ciudad porque no hay una piscina y una biblioteca.

c. Vivo en Londres. En mi ciudad hay museos y también teatros.

d. Vivo en un pueblo es pequeño. Hay tiendas, pero no hay cine.

e. En mi pueblo hay una farmacia y vivo una estación de tren.

f. ¿Qué hay en tu pueblo? En mi pueblo hay una playa bonita.

7. Narrow Listening. Gap-fill

a. Vivo____ una ciudad __________ en Francia. En mi__________________ hay un ________, una _____________ y ____________________. Me gusta _____ barrio porque es ______________ y bonito.

cine	mi	grande	piscina	barrio	tranquilo	en	restaurantes

b. Soy de ____________, pero vivo en ______________, en un ___________ pequeño. Me _____________ mi barrio porque es _____________, pero _____ poco ____________.

animado	Alemania	pueblo	encanta	ruidoso	un	España

8. Listening Slalom

Listen in Spanish and pick the equivalent English words from each column.

e.g. En mi pueblo hay un cine

Colour in the boxes for each sentence in a different colour.

e.g.	***In my town***	because it is big.	swimming pools.
a.	In my city there is	***there is***	There are restaurants and shops.
b.	I live in Barcelona.	a sports centre	***a cinema.***
c.	In my town there are	a cinema,	and a castle.
d.	I love my neighbourhood	There is a beach	and a museum.
e.	I like my town because	shops, but there are not	square, but there isn't a stadium.
f.	In my town there isn't	it is pretty. There is a	but there is a library.

Unit 10. I can say what's in my town: READING

1. Read and put the syllables in the cells in the correct order

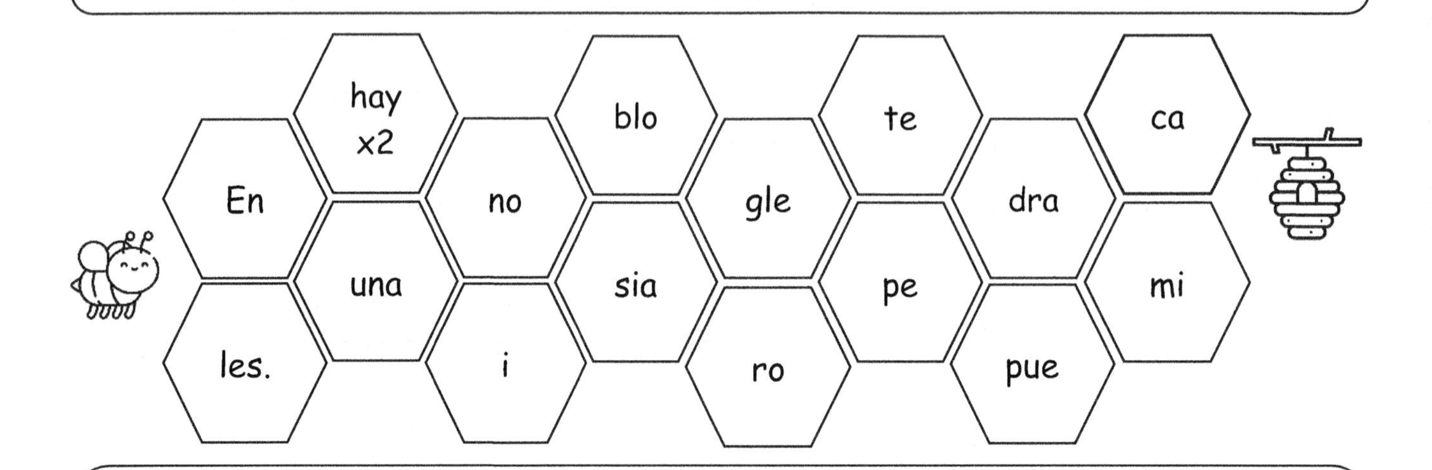

a. In my town there is a church, but there are no cathedrals.

E__ m__ p__________ h____ u____ i____________, p______
n__ h____ c____________________.

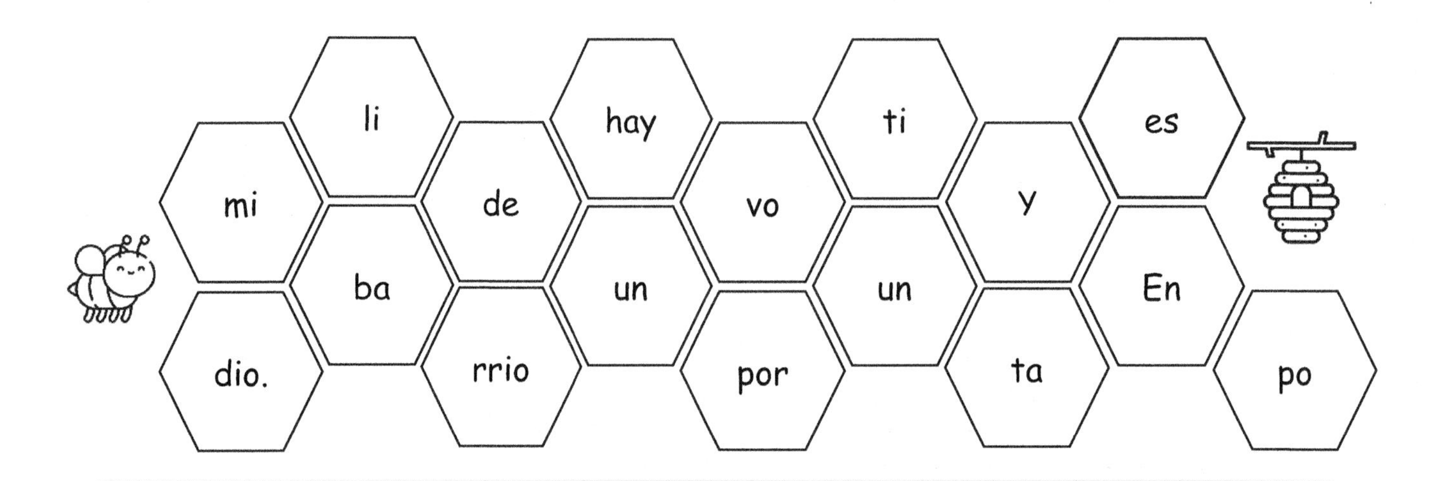

b. In my neighbourhood there is a sports centre and a stadium.

E__ m__ b__________ h____ u__ p________________________
y u__ e____________.

2. True or false

A. Read the paragraphs below and then answer True or False

Hola, me llamo **Joaquín**. Tengo catorce años. Vivo en Berlín, la capital de Alemania. Me gusta mi ciudad porque es grande y turística, pero es muy ruidosa. En mi barrio hay una librería, un estadio y un centro comercial, pero no hay cines.

Hola, me llamo **Patricia**. Soy de Francia, pero vivo en España. En Madrid, la capital de España, normalmente hace calor en verano. Me gusta mi ciudad porque es turística y bonita. En mi barrio hay una estación de tren y un parque, pero no hay estadios.

	True	False
a. **Joaquín** is 14 years old.		
b. He doesn't like his city.		
c. His city is small and touristic.		
d. In his neighbourhood there is a stadium.		
e. In his neighbourhood there is a cinema.		
f. **Patricia** is from Spain.		
g. She lives in France.		
h. In Madrid it is normally cold in summer.		
i. In her neighbourhood there is a train station.		
j. In her neighbourhood there are no stadiums.		

B. Find in the texts above the Spanish for:

a. The capital of Germany.

b. There is a train station.

c. I like my city.

d. There are no cinemas.

3. Tick or Cross

A. Read the texts. Tick the box if you find the words in the text, cross it if you do not find them.

- Hola, me llamo **Gisela**.

Tengo siete años. Soy de España y vivo en un pueblo pequeño que se llama Ronda. En mi pueblo hay un castillo, un museo y una iglesia, pero no hay estación de tren.

- Hola, me llamo **Ramón**.

Tengo seis años. Soy de Italia y vivo en una ciudad que se llama Roma. Me gusta porque es bonita. En mi barrio hay un parque, una librería y una piscina, pero no hay cines.

	✓	X
a. Tengo siete años.		
b. Soy de Francia.		
c. Un pueblo grande.		
d. Hay un castillo.		
e. No hay iglesias.		
f. Que se llama.		

g. I am 7 years old.		
h. I am from Italy.		
i. Because it is big.		
j. In my neighbourhood.		
k. A swimming pool.		
l. There are no parks.		

B. Find the Spanish in the texts above

a. A small town called. ______________________________

b. There is no train station. ______________________________

c. I live in a city called Rome. ______________________________

d. In my neighbourhood there is a park. ______________________________

e. But there are no cinemas. ______________________________

4. Language Detective

- Me llamo **Mario.** Tengo doce años. Soy de Portugal, pero vivo en París, la capital de Francia. En París normalmente hace buen tiempo. Me gusta porque hay parques y catedrales, y el estadio del 'Paris Saint-Germain' (PSG).

- Me llamo **Roberto.** Tengo trece años. Soy de Italia, pero vivo en Madrid, la capital de España. En Madrid, en verano, hace calor. Me encanta la ciudad porque es turística. También hay museos y el estadio del Real Madrid.

- Hola, me llamo **Mariana**. Tengo once años. Soy de Escocia, pero vivo en Londres, la capital de Inglaterra. En Londres normalmente llueve. Me gusta porque hay tiendas, pero es una ciudad muy ruidosa.

A. Find someone who...

a. ...is 13 years old.

b. ...lives in England.

c. ...lives in a city with museums.

d. ...doesn't mention a stadium.

e. ...lives in a city with parks.

f. ...lives in a noisy city.

g. ...is from Scotland.

B. Put a cross in the box and underline the corresponding Spanish translation. Two are odd.

~~I am from Italy.~~	There are parks.	It usually rains in London.
I love it because it is touristic.	The stadium of PSG	In summer it is warm in Madrid.
But I live in England.	But I live in London	The weather is normally good in Paris.
There are also museums.	I don't like my city	It's a very noisy city.

Unit 10. I can say what's in my town: WRITING

1. Spelling

a. U _ _ e _ _ _ _ _ _ _ de tr _ n. *A train station.*

b. U _ e _ _ _ d _ _. *A stadium.*

c. U _ _ p _ _ _ _ _ _ _. *A swimming pool.*

d. U _ r _ _ _ _ u _ _ _ t _. *A restaurant.*

e. U _ _ b _ b _ _ _ t _ _ _. *A library.*

f. U _ p _ l _ _ _ p _ _ _ _ v _. *A sports centre.*

g. H _ _ u _ p _ _ _ u _. *There is a park.*

h. N_ h _ _ t _ _ _ d _ _. *There are no shops.*

2. Anagrams

a. yaH nu querap. *There is a park.*

b. Hya nua tredalca. *There is a cathedral.*

c. oN hay scinapis. *There are no swimming pools.*

d. Hya reutstaranes. *There are restaurants.*

3. Gapped Translation

a. En mi barrio hay un polideportivo y un estadio.

In my ______________ there is a _______ _______ and a stadium.

b. En mi pueblo hay una plaza grande.

In my _________ there is a big __________.

c. Vivo en Londres. En Londres hay catedrales y castillos.

I ______ in London. In London ______ are cathedrals and _______.

d. ¿Qué hay en tu barrio? Hay una plaza bonita.

What ___ there in your neighbourhood? There is a pretty ________.

e. En mi ciudad hay una iglesia y una biblioteca.

In my _______ there is a _________ and a _____________.

4. Split Sentences

a. Hay — 1. ciudad.

b. En mi — 2. mi pueblo.

c. En — 3. gusta mi ciudad.

d. Me — 4. una estación de tren.

e. Hay una — 5. plaza.

f. Porque es — 6. Francia.

g. Vivo en — 7. bonita.

a	b	c	d	e	f	g
4						

5. Rock Climbing

Starting from the bottom, pick one chunk from each row to translate the sentences below.

a.	b.	c.	d.	e.
y una catedral.	pero hay un supermercado.	hay cines.	y un castillo.	y una piscina.
porque no	un polideportivo,	una biblioteca	un estadio	Hay una plaza bonita
en tu pueblo?	hay	no hay	mi barrio	hay
En mi barrio	En mi ciudad	En mi pueblo	¿Qué hay	No me gusta

a. In my neighbourhood there is a library and a castle.

____

b. In my city there is a stadium and a cathedral.

____

c. In my town there is not a sports centre, but there is a supermarket.

____

d. What is there in your town? There is a pretty square and a swimming pool.

____

e. I don't like my neighbourhood because there are no cinemas.

____

6. Fill in the gaps

a. Hola, me llamo Ramón. Tengo ________ años. Soy de ________, pero vivo en Londres. Me gusta porque es muy _________. En mi ___________ hay una _____________ y ___ estadio.

grande	Italia	nueve	un	barrio	piscina

b. Hola, me llamo Nieves. Soy de América, pero _________ en Mallorca. _____ gusta porque __________________ hace calor. En ____ ciudad __________ una iglesia y _________ hay piscinas.

normalmente	Me	vivo	hay	también	mi

7. Tangled Translation

a. Write the Spanish words in English to complete the translation

Hello, **me llamo Ana. Soy de** England, **pero** I live **en Italia.** I speak Italian **y alemán.** In Italy, **normalmente** the **tiempo** is good. **En mi barrio** there is **una panadería** and shops, **pero** there is no **estación de tren.**

b. Write the English words in Spanish to complete the translation

Buenos días, **my name is** Juan. Tengo **twelve** años. Vivo **in Germany,** en la capital que se llama **Berlin. I like it** porque es **very big** y turística. **In my** barrio **there are** una farmacia **and a shop** pero no hay **bakery.**

¿Dónde vives **and what** hay **in your** ciudad?

8. Sentence Puzzle

Put the Spanish words in the correct order

a. barrio En mi tiendas hay también supermercados. y

In my neighbourhood there are shops and also supermarkets.

b. ¿Qué tu pueblo Hay hay en piscina una y plaza. una

What is there in your town? There is a swimming pool and a square.

c. estaciones de tren. hay catedral, una ciudad pero hay no En mi

In my city there is a cathedral, but there are no train stations.

d. bonito Mi pueblo porque hay restaurantes. y tiendas es

My town is pretty because there are shops and restaurants.

9. Guided Translation

a. H_______, m___ l_________ M_____________. V________ e_____ u___ c_______________ b_________ q___ s____ l______________ P________.

Hi, my name is Mafalda. I live in a pretty city which is called Paris.

b. V_______ e____ u____ c_________ b_________. E___ m___ c_________ h____ t_____________, p________ n____ h_________ p______________.

I live in a pretty city. In my city there are shops, but there are no swimming pools.

c. E___ m___ b__________ h____ u____ c____________ y u____ i________, p_________ n____ h____ p__________. E___ m____ a_________________.

In my neighbourhood there is a school and a church, but there are no parks. It is very boring.

10. Staircase Translation

Starting from the top, translate each chunk into Spanish.
Write the sentences in the grid below.

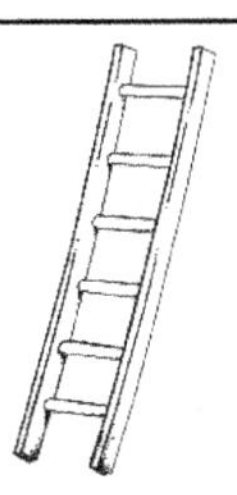

a.	I like	my city.				
b.	I don't like	my town because	there are no cinemas.			
c.	In my neighbourhood	there is a library, but	there are no sports centres	It is pretty.		
d.	In my city	there is a stadium, but	there is no train station.	It is noisy	and also touristic.	
e.	In my town	there is a church, but	there are no cathedrals.	It is small	and also calm,	but it's noisy.

Answers / Respuestas	
a.	
b.	
c.	
d.	
e.	

Challenge / Desafío

Can you create 2 more sentences using the words in the staircase grid above?

☆	
☆	

No Snakes No Ladders

SALIDA	1 Vivo en	2 Vivo en Barcelona	3 Mi pueblo	4 Mi ciudad	5 Me encanta mi pueblo	6 ¿Dónde vives?	7 En mi barrio
15 Porque no es feo	14 Es tranquilo	13 Es bonita	12 Me gusta mi ciudad porque	11 Hay tiendas	10 Parques y restau-rantes	9 No hay un polidepor-tivo	8 Hay una piscina
16 Vivo en Londres	17 Mi pueblo es ruidoso	18 Hay un super-mercado	19 Y una estación de tren	20 También hay un parque	21 Odio mi ciudad	22 Mi pueblo es pequeño	23 Vivo en Marbella
LLEGADA	30 Mi ciudad es animada	29 Mi pueblo es turístico	28 Porque es grande	27 No me gusta mi ciudad	26 No hay un cine	25 Un castillo y una catedral	24 Hay una iglesia

No Snakes No Ladders

SALIDA	1 I live in	2 I live in Barcelona	3 My town	4 My city	5 I love my town	6 Where do you live?	7 In my neighbour-hood
15 Because it is not ugly (m)	14 It is quiet (m)	13 It is pretty (f)	12 I like my city because	11 There are shops	10 Parks and restau-rants	9 There isn't a sports centre	8 There is a swimming pool
16 I live in London	17 My town is noisy	18 There is a super-market	19 And a train station	20 There is also a park	21 I hate my city	22 My town is small	23 I live in Marbella
LLEGADA	30 My city is lively	29 My town is touristic	28 Because it is big	27 I don't like my city	26 There isn't a cinema	25 A castle and a cathedral	24 There is a church

UNIT 10 - EN MI PUEBLO

LISTENING

1. Listen and tick the word you hear
a. 2 (plaza) b. 1 (cine) c. 2 (no hay) d. 3 (teatros) e. 2 (iglesias)

2. Faulty Echo.
e.g. En mi ***pueblo*** *hay un cine. (publo)*
a. En mi **ciudad** hay una iglesia. (cuidad)
b. En mi pueblo **hay** una biblioteca. (hey)
c. En mi ciudad hay restaurantes y **parques.** (parqwes)
d. En mi pueblo no hay **piscinas.** (pisquinas)
e. En mi pueblo hay un polideportivo y un **castillo.** (castilo)
f. En mi ciudad hay una **plaza** pero no hay un museo. (plazza)

3. Listen and complete with the missing vowel
a. Mi pueblo b. Una plaza c. Una piscina d. Mi ciudad e. Un cine
f. Un museo g. Un polideportivo h. Una panadería i. Una iglesia j. ¿Hay una plaza?

4. Complete with the missing syllables in the box below
a. Un superm**er**cado b. Un tea**tro** c. Tien**das** d. Co**le**gios e. Un par**que**
f. Una far**ma**cia g. Una bi**blio**teca h. Un casti**llo** i. Res**tau**rantes j. Mi **ciu**dad

5. Fill in the grid with the information in English
a. Museum ; beach b. Shops, restaurants ; stadium
c. Schools, parks ; swimming pools d. Supermarket, library ; theatre

6. Spot the Intruder. Identify the word in each sentence the speaker is NOT saying
a. Un b. No c. También d. Es e. Vivo f. Bonita

7. Narrow Listening. Gap-fill
a. Vivo **en** una ciudad **grande** en Francia. En mi **barrio** hay un **cine**, una **piscina** y **restaurantes**. Me gusta **mi** barrio porque es **tranquilo** y bonito.
b. Soy de **Alemania,** pero vivo en **España**, en un **pueblo** pequeño. Me **encanta** mi barrio porque es **animado,** pero **un** poco **ruidoso.**

8. Listening Slalom
a. En mi ciudad hay un polideportivo y un museo.
b. Vivo en Barcelona. Hay una playa y un castillo.
c. En mi pueblo hay tiendas, pero no hay piscinas.
d. Me encanta mi barrio porque es grande. Hay restaurantes y tiendas.
e. Me gusta mi pueblo porque es bonito. Hay una plaza, pero no hay un estadio.
f. En mi pueblo no hay un cine, pero hay una biblioteca.

READING

1. Sylla-Bees

a. En mi pueblo hay una iglesia, pero no hay catedrales.
b. En mi barrio hay un polideportivo y un estadio.

2. True or False

A. Read the paragraphs and decide if the statements are True or False

a. True b. False (he likes) c. False (big and touristic)
d. True e. False (no cinemas) f. False (she is from France)
g. False (in Spain) h. False (it is warm) i. True j. True

B. Find in the text above the Spanish for:

a. La capital de Alemania b. Hay una estación de tren. c. Me gusta mi ciudad.
d. No hay cines.

3. Tick or Cross

A. Read the text. Tick the box if you find the words in the text, cross it if you do not find them

a. ✓ b. X c. X d. ✓ e. X f. ✓ g. X h. ✓ i. X j. ✓ k. ✓ l. X

B. Find the Spanish in the text above

a. Un pueblo pequeño que se llama... b. No hay estación de tren.
c. Vivo en una ciudad que se llama Roma. d. En mi barrio hay un parque.
e. Pero no hay cines.

4. Language Detective

A. Find someone who...

a. Roberto b. Mariana c. Roberto d. Mariana e. Mario f. Mariana g. Mariana

B. Odd two out:

But I live in England. - I don't like my city. (two odd chunks)

WRITING

1. Spelling

a. Una estación de tren b. Un estadio c. Una piscina d. Un restaurante
e. Una biblioteca f. Un polideportivo g. Hay un parque h. No hay tiendas

2. Anagrams

a. Hay un parque. b. Hay una catedral. c. No hay piscinas. d. Hay restaurantes.

3. Gapped Translation

a. In my **neighbourhood** there is a **sports centre** and a stadium.
b. In my **town** there is a big **square.**
c. I **live** in London. In London **there** are cathedrals and **castles.**
d. What **is** there in your neighbourhood? There is a pretty **square.**
e. In my **city** there is a **church** and a **library.**

4. Split Sentences

a. 4 b. 1 c. 2 d. 3 e. 5 f. 7 g. 6

5. Rock Climbing

a. En mi barrio hay una biblioteca y un castillo.
b. En mi ciudad hay un estadio y una catedral.
c. En mi pueblo no hay un polideportivo, pero hay un supermercado.
d. ¿Qué hay en tu pueblo? Hay una plaza bonita y una piscina.
e. No me gusta mi barrio porque no hay cines.

6. Fill in the Gaps

a. Hola, me llamo Ramón. Tengo **nueve** años. Soy de **Italia,** pero vivo en Londres. Me gusta porque es muy **grande**. En mi **barrio** hay una **piscina** y **un** estadio.
b. Hola, me llamo Nieves. Soy de América, pero **vivo** en Mallorca. **Me** gusta porque **normalmente** hace calor. En **mi** ciudad **hay** una iglesia. **También** hay piscinas.

7. Tangled Translation

a. Hello, **my name is Ana. I am from** England, **but** I live **in Italy.** I speak Italian **and German.** In Italy, **usually** the **weather** is good. **In my neighbourhood** there is **a bakery** and shops, **but** there is no **train station.**

b. Buenos días, **me llamo** Juan. Tengo **doce** años. Vivo **en Alemania,** en la capital, que se llama **Berlín. Me gusta** porque es **muy grande** y turística. **En mi** barrio **hay** una farmacia **y una tienda,** pero no hay **panadería.** ¿Dónde vives **y qué** hay **en tu** ciudad?

8. Sentence Puzzle

a. En mi barrio hay tiendas y también supermercados.
b. ¿Qué hay en tu pueblo? Hay una piscina y una plaza.
c. En mi ciudad hay una catedral, pero no hay estaciones de tren.
d. Mi pueblo es bonito porque hay tiendas y restaurantes.

9. Guided Translation

a. **Hola**, me **llamo Mafalda. Vivo** en **una ciudad bonita** que se **llama París.**
b. **Vivo** en **una ciudad bonita.** En mi **ciudad** hay **tiendas, pero** no **hay piscinas.**
c. **En** mi **barrio hay un** co**legio** y **una iglesia, pero** no **hay parques. Es** muy a**burrido.**

10. Staircase Translation

a. Me gusta mi ciudad.
b. No me gusta mi pueblo porque no hay cines.
c. En mi barrio hay una biblioteca, pero no hay polideportivos. Es bonito.
d. En mi ciudad hay un estadio, pero no hay estación de tren. Es ruidosa y también turística.
e. En mi pueblo hay una iglesia, pero no hay catedrales. Es pequeño y también tranquilo, pero es ruidoso.

Printed in Great Britain
by Amazon

82497404R00113

Mi día favorito es My favourite day is	el lunes Mon el martes Tues el miércoles Wed el jueves Thurs el viernes Fri (saturday-sábado) (Sunday-domingo) Semana-week	porque because	estudio I study estudiamos We study	dibujo art música music teatro drama educación física PE tecnología Design & Technology informática IT inglés English francés French español Spanish historia geografía religión ciencias sciences matemáticas

Me encanta I love Me gusta I like No me gusta I don't like No me gusta nada I don't like at all	el	dibujo/teatro/inglés/francés/español/	porque	es it is un poco a bit/ bastante quite/muy very	aburrido/divertido/práctico/ difícil/ fácil/útil/ inútil/interesante
	la	música/ educación física/ tecnología/ informática/ historia/ geografía/ religión			aburrida/divertida/práctica/ difícil/ fácil/útil/ inútil/interesante
Me encantan Me gustan No me gustan No me gustan nada	los	idiomas		son they are un poco/ bastante/muy	aburridos/divertidos/prácticos/ difíciles/ fáciles/útiles/ inútiles/interesantes
	las	ciencias/matemáticas			aburridas/divertidas/prácticas/ difíciles/ fáciles/útiles/ inútiles/interesantes

y (and)
pero (but)